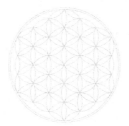

PRAISE FOR "THE WAY OF FERTILITY"

"*The Way of Fertility* is a woman's journey into her body-mind-spirit wholeness to rekindle hope for fertility health. Blending ancient wisdom and practices with modern science, Michelle walks the reader through practical suggestions for regaining physical and emotional balance and alignment to support reproductive energy."

Deanna Minich, PhD, nutrition scientist and author of *Whole Detox*

"Michelle Oravitz opens the treasure chest of ancient wisdom to reveal pathways to our greatest human call, parenting. Spiritual awakening prepares us to inherit the ultimate love that nourishes the deep soul of a child."

Lisa Miller, PhD, *New York Times* best-selling author of *The Spiritual Child* and *The Awakened Brain*

"Through her insights, Michelle bridges ancient wisdom with modern research, showing how the right practices can enhance reproductive potential. She offers practical guidance to help you every step of the way. This is a must-read for those longing to grow their families."

Jessica Ortner, *New York Times* best-selling author and creator of the Tapping Solution App

"Michelle is miraculous in her ability to distill thousands of years of ancient wisdom into an easy-to-follow text for modern, thoughtful, and conscious women who are ready to get and stay pregnant. While insanely effective, her methodology isn't about quick, superficial fixes. It's about real, sustainable solutions for before, during, and after your pregnancy. If you are serious about conceiving, you will snatch this book up, curl up with it, and get to work on making simple changes that will indeed change your life. Your baby will thank you."

Rosanne Austin, fertility coach and author of *Am I the Reason I'm Not Getting Pregnant?*

"*This* is the book that I needed to read when I was on my fertility journey!! Michelle has done an incredible job of weaving ancient wisdom, relatable stories, and practical exercises into one place. I love the gentle approach she uses to help you transition from being at war with your body and trying to control it to creating harmony, alignment, and understanding. It is the perfect combination of practical and woo-woo. I'd highly recommend this book to anyone who is trying to conceive and is feeling disconnected or frustrated with their body and wants to feel more at peace. For me, this is the permission slip we all need to start being kinder to ourselves."

Jennifer Robertson, fertility coach and author of *The Injustice of Infertility*

THE WAY OF FERTILITY

AWAKEN YOUR REPRODUCTIVE POTENTIAL
THROUGH THE POWER OF ANCIENT WISDOM

MICHELLE ORAVITZ

Published 2024

ISBN 978-1-954991-04-0 (paperback)

ISBN 978-1-954991-03-3 (eBook)

For privacy reasons, some names may have been changed.

Although the author and publisher have made every effort to ensure that the information in this book was correct at press time, the author and publisher do not assume and hereby disclaim any liability to any party for any loss, damage, or disruption caused by errors or omissions, whether such errors or omissions result from negligence, accident, or any other cause.

This book is not intended as a substitute for the medical advice of physicians. The reader should regularly consult a physician in matters relating to their health, particularly with respect to any symptoms that may require diagnosis or medical attention.

Please note that the author and publisher don't make any guarantees about the results of the information applied in *The Way of Fertility*. This book shares educational and informational resources that are intended to help you succeed in getting pregnant. You nevertheless need to know that your ultimate success or failure will be the result of your own efforts, your particular situation, and innumerable other circumstances beyond the author and publisher's knowledge and control.

Visit author's website at www.michelleoravitz.com.

Edited by Yna Davis, Publish with Pleasure

Proofread by Andrae Smith Jr., Lantern Literary

To the strong lineage of women that I was blessed to come from: My grandmother, who, with her captivating stories, awakened a spark of wisdom and a fascination with natural healing within me at an early age. My mother, who fought for me even before I entered her womb and who poured her love and heart into raising my brother and me despite the challenges she faced. And my beautiful girls, who inspire and teach me on a regular basis, and who I know will carry on the legacy and essence of the strong women we came from.

To the men in my life: My father, whose last name means "teacher" and who taught me the importance of always staying true to myself. I know your essence is still with us, celebrating each achievement we are fortunate enough to experience. My husband, the love of my life, whose support and belief in me inspired a feeling that I can do anything and who makes life pure magic when he's at my side. And my favorite (and only) brother, who always felt more like a twin—our bond is something I will forever cherish.

CONTENTS

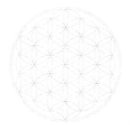

A Gift for You

Thank you for choosing to take this journey with me on *The Way of Fertility*!
I have a created a free list of resources that will be referenced in this book. Head over to https://www.michelleoravitz.com/ thewayoffertilityresources to get access!

FOREWORD

"Conception is less about what to do and more about how to be."

That sentence says it all. And that sentence is the primary reason you need to read this book.

Michelle and I see fertility the same way: fertility is not an on/off switch; rather, it's a state of health. And health is more than just your lab markers or your age. Health includes spiritual health, emotional health, physical health, and nutritional health. Harnessing and shifting fertility is about small consistent shifts; it's about your way of being. In *The Way of Fertility*, Michelle captures the essence of how to *be* more fertile. Yes, she also gives you plenty of actionable steps to take. But those steps are not just things you tick off on your to-do list; they are micro-shifts that are rooted in your state of being that will impact your entire way of life and wellness at the root level.

I've been helping women get and stay pregnant for two decades. I wish I could say there were five specific things one could do to go from having fertility challenges to being healthily pregnant, but fertility doesn't work that way. When someone is dealing with fertility challenges, their body is speaking and giving signals that it's not at its fullest potential. Rest assured, you can shift your body back to its thriving state, and fertility can be improved. In *The Way of Fertility*, Michelle gives you not only the tools to make that happen but a road map to the way of being that best supports your health and fertility. Even more, she gives you a road map to help you find your way back to yourself, including how to best nourish and support yourself so that this baby can come through and be nourished in the same way.

The approach Michelle takes in her practice and in this book is the cornerstone not just to thriving fertility, but to a better way of life and, ultimately, to a more abundant future for you and your growing family. This book should be in the hands of every single person dealing with fertility challenges. It's chock-full of wisdom, and you will reference it even after you get to the other side of your fertility journey.

Dig in, take notes, and allow yourself to reclaim your fertile nature.

Sending you all baby dust and love.

Aimee E. Raupp
Best-selling author of *Yes, You Can Get Pregnant* and *The Egg Quality Diet*

AUTHOR'S NOTE

I wanted to take a moment to thank you for taking this sacred journey with me. Each chapter, story, and lesson you will read has been written with the intention of not only providing knowledge, but also providing a transformative impact on the reader. You'll notice the flower of life at the beginning of each chapter; this ancient sacred geometry symbol represents creation and growth. Its geometric pattern reflects the emergence of an embryo and embodies the essence of new life. I purposefully chose this meaningful symbol with the intention to bless you with fertility and new life as your eyes repeatedly gaze on it at the beginning of each chapter. I invite you to engage with the wisdom and lessons of this book with a sense of curiosity, allowing the information to awaken a portal to the infinite possibilities that reside within you.

INTRODUCTION

What if I told you that your thoughts, words, and actions can directly impact your fertility health?

If you have been exhausting all your options as you try to get pregnant, are feeling unsure about what to do next, and have found yourself at a point where you are grasping for any shred of hope and don't believe it's possible to thrive while you're on your fertility journey, *this book is for you!*

As an acupuncturist specializing in fertility health, I have found that when many of my patients first come to me, they say that they've done everything they can, but when I ask them how they are supporting their own personal energy and well-being, it becomes apparent that they haven't been prioritizing their self-care and are often on the bottom of their own lists.

Many couples come to me with hope for an outcome of pregnancy. I let them know that, to reach that outcome, they can't miss an important priority: returning to their natural state of well-being. We cannot bypass the path that leads to the goal. Focusing only on the goal causes us to miss the train that will take us there. There are no shortcuts to vitality; we need to follow the signs that the highest intelligence is showing us in order to truly understand what our bodies, minds, and spirits are asking of us. What many are surprised by once they realize this is that the fertility journey doesn't need to be filled with suffering and that, by encouraging a state of joy, they consequently begin to improve their reproductive health.

In short, conception is less about what to do and more about how to be. This book is intended to show you how to shift from *seeking* fertility to *embodying* fertility by claiming your innate fertile essence. It shares wisdom from Chinese medicine and Taoism and gifts from other ancient wisdom teachings that provide us invaluable tools to evoke a fertile nature of being, and it incorporates my own intuitive learnings from my experience working in the world of fertility. The wisdom of ancient teachings shows us how to live in ways that align our bodies with the rhythms of nature so that we can arrive at a state of optimal vitality that supports a fertile body. I have seen over and over how a state of alignment and flow not only creates a sense of joy (even before the baby comes) but also enhances fertility.

So many women have come to me feeling hopeless after being told that they couldn't get pregnant on their own. They were told that they had a very low reserve or that they were approaching menopause, only to end up getting pregnant and giving birth to healthy babies naturally. I have witnessed these stories time and time again—and so many of these stories defy the predictions these women were given. This lit a fire in me to spread a message of hope, as so many are given a sense of hopelessness about their reproductive potential.

My mission is to get this message out: if you are in your reproductive years, you are hardwired to conceive. Your reproductive health is a reflection of your overall health. Overall health and healing arise when we live in accordance with the Tao, or The Way. This doesn't just relate to our bodies but to our thoughts, words, and actions.

In this book, I will cover what it means to live in harmony with your innate nature and why it's so simple to get back into this balance. Your body has been designed to find its "healing zone" because nature always moves in the direction of health and vitality. You were born to procreate, and your body has a detailed blueprint to move you in that direction. If you are struggling, it may be because you have been moving away from your natural balance by living against your natural rhythms.

The Way of Fertility highlights the importance of your state of being when it comes to overall vitality and reproductive health. This is not to say that people who are having fertility challenges are to blame in any way for those challenges. In many cases, reproductive challenges are simply a symptom of imbalances of the body, mind, and spirit. Usually, the first response for improving fertility challenges is to address the body, but in *The Way of Fertility*, we focus on something that is often overlooked, which is the intersection of the mind, spirit, and our vital relationship with the natural world around us—specifically how, ultimately, those unseen aspects of ourselves reflect and impact the body's fertility.

This book is intended to direct you on an inward journey to uncover hidden blocks that might be getting in the way of your conception. You will learn powerful exercises and scientific explanations of the power of many ancient practices that were once considered "woo-woo." You will also learn how to harness the powerful rhythms of nature by entraining and aligning your body to its intelligent and naturally fertile essence. These exercises are designed to kindle a flame of transformation that will inevitably lead the way to igniting your fertile potential. They will show you how to connect with the part of yourself that holds all the answers and is waiting to guide you on the way of fertility. I have carefully crafted every single piece of the following chapters as intentional catalysts to bring you closer to your dream of having a child. Thank you for sharing your journey with me. Now let's get started!

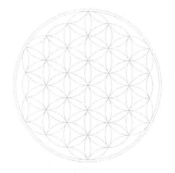

CHAPTER 1

Reclaiming Our Fertile Nature

My own conception did not come easy, as my mom faced challenges getting pregnant with me. She also experienced many scares while carrying me, including severe nausea, dehydration, and weight loss, and feared throughout that the pregnancy wouldn't make it to term. She often reminds me of how much she fought for me to be here. Years before my conception, she saw me in a dream, a curly-haired girl (I'm the only family member with curly hair) skipping along happily. The fact that I'm here to write this book is a testament to a result of a woman who knew in her heart she was meant to have me and answered that calling deep within her soul.

In my early years growing up, I was exposed to the ideas of natural healing as my grandmother often shared with me natural remedies to alleviate certain conditions. I was always enamored by the wisdom she imparted about the benefits that certain foods and plants had on our health. She told me that we are meant to ingest the food and plants that were created by our own creator. She often reiterated that we had all the natural means we needed to heal ourselves.

I remember getting sick frequently as a child, and I'm not sure if it was because we moved around a lot. When I first began menstruating at the age of thirteen, I noticed that each of my periods came two or three months after the last. I thought this would eventually change, but the irregularity followed me for many years.

When I was seventeen, my mom decided to take me to a gynecologist, and I remember feeling a sense of hope that he would know exactly how to resolve my irregular periods. Much to my surprise, he prescribed me birth control pills. When I asked why I was given the birth control pills if I wasn't sexually active, my doctor said they would give me regular monthly periods.

"What will happen when I get off of them?" I asked.

"You will go back to having irregular periods."

I was dumbfounded and extremely disappointed by the exchange, which I had hoped would play out so differently.

For the eight years following, I went on and off birth control pills. I didn't want to stay on them long term because somehow, I knew they might be harming my body. I look back and realize that the influences of my grandmother's wisdom and my own intuition were trying to speak to me, but I was only hearing them sporadically. My body often felt exhausted, and my circadian rhythm was misaligned. I regularly stayed up late, and, if left to my own devices, I slept until 2 or 3 in the afternoon. I would often feel depressed, and when my period did come, I would experience severe PMS and cramping.

I continued visiting doctors and was given the same response repeatedly: there was nothing I could do to change my cycle except take the birth control pill. This information still didn't sit well with me, but I struggled to find an alternative answer.

When I turned twenty-five, it dawned on me that something different had to be done. I went backpacking in Europe and Cuba for several months, and during that time, I was off the birth control pill. I didn't get my period at all during that whole time away. Maybe I was more attuned to these things because I was getting older, or maybe being away made me more aware of how much time was passing, but this felt like a wake-up call that I needed to do something about my irregular periods. During my time in Cuba, I received a reading from a Santería medium, and he told me that he sensed a blockage in my pelvic region and that I should look into it. At the time, I didn't make any connection that this might be referring to my menstrual cycle. He also mentioned that I would meet a tall older male figure who would change the course of my life.

When I moved back to New York after my trip, I expressed my concern to my mom, who told me she had heard about an acupuncturist who specialized in gynecology.

His name was Dr. Li, and he worked out of his home in Rego Park, Queens. I remember driving to his house with my mom and walking down some stairs to get to a side entrance. As I did, I felt a sense of relief; I intuitively knew that I was making an aligned choice for my reproductive health.

Dr. Li answered the door with the biggest smile, welcoming my mom and me in. I'll never forget the overwhelming scent of Chinese herbs and the sight of his bookshelf filled with medical texts. It didn't register for me at the time, but Dr. Li seemed to fit the description the Santería medium in Cuba had given me; he was older and happened to have a tall stature.

I answered the thorough list of questions on Dr. Li's new patient form. He then invited me to sit down by his desk, took my pulse, looked at my tongue, and asked me more questions. I don't remember ever before having to answer so many in-depth questions at a physician's office! The questions dove into subjects such as the shape of my poop, the color of my menstrual blood, and the level of my overall energy.

Dr. Li explained how traditional Chinese medicine viewed the importance of a woman's menstrual cycle and how it reflects a woman's overall health. After my acupuncture treatment, Dr. Li filled a paper bag with Chinese herbs and gave me directions for how to cook them. To my delight, I came home that day and got my period! I was amazed that my period had emerged after just one treatment, especially given my twelve years of irregular periods. Various symptoms that I had regarded as normal started to dissipate. I learned that the cramps, PMS, acne, and mood swings that I experienced when off the birth control pill weren't just not normal; they were signs that my body was screaming at me to pay attention.

My Own Coming into Alignment

As I continued treatments with Dr. Li, I observed even more symptoms alleviating. I began noticing that my confidence increased, and I didn't ruminate like I had used to about the challenges that I experienced at work. I felt more at ease in my body, and my skin cleared up. I was so surprised that, though I had just gone in for the one symptom, my period irregularity, I began feeling better in many other ways. I realized that, for so many years, I had been disconnected from even recognizing my symptoms because feeling imbalanced had become my normal state.

Indeed, for years, I had ignored my body's cues. I had allowed it to be hungry so I could look good in my bikini. I had stayed up late because I wanted to hang out with my friends. I had drunk alcohol because I wanted to numb my uncomfortable social anxiety. I had bypassed my inner wisdom to please everyone around me. Why? . . . Because I didn't know better.

My story is the story of many. I was so disconnected from my inner wisdom, and frankly, I didn't think my inner voice was worth listening to back then. I wanted to be someone else, the perfect woman on the magazine cover or my own mental ideal. The person I wanted to be was completely unlike the real me . . . and my body was screaming out because my rejection of its authenticity reverberated into every cell, molecule, and atom that supported my physical expression.

Once I awakened my awareness that the way I'd been living wasn't acceptable anymore, I started getting clues about how to resolve it. I realized that my physical state was a reflection of my internal state, that my beliefs about myself were not separate from my reproductive health. I realized that every aspect of my life—my work, relationships, and internal dialogue—all mattered and impacted my physical and emotional well-being.

This realization eventually impacted how I approach my patients when it comes to getting a complete picture of their lives and how the parts impact the whole when it comes to their fertility.

As predicted by the Santería medium in Cuba, Dr. Li did, in fact, end up changing the course of my life. He resolved my fertility health before it occurred to me that my menstrual cycle would have a role in my future pregnancies. Had our paths not crossed, I imagine I would've had a very difficult challenge growing my own family. It was the incredible alignment and healing that I received in being a patient of Dr. Li's that led me to study traditional Chinese medicine and eventually specialize in fertility health. This work is not a job for me; it is my mission.

Finding Our Way

Traditional Chinese medicine is founded on the teachings of Taoism, which translates as "The Way." "The Way" refers to the golden path of harmony that nature is designed to follow. This golden path is another way of describing optimal alignment for sustaining balance. Everything nature does is to create this harmonious balance. Day dissolves into night and night dissolves into day so that the living elements have just enough of what they need to thrive. This is depicted in the two opposing forces of yin and yang, which I will describe in more detail in chapter 4. A woman's reproductive cycle is a beautiful example of the harmony that takes place in the body as the cycle ebbs and flows with its own seasons.

Our bodies are designed to thrive and procreate to continue our natural evolutionary progression and survival as a species. When this natural process gets disrupted, such as when one experiences challenges conceiving, there is a reason for this, and it needs to be uncovered. If we weren't designed this way, our species would have ceased to exist a long time ago. Keep in mind that human beings didn't always have doctors to rely on to let us know what was happening with our bodies, and our bodies' innate communication has always played a role in our survival.

During my twelve-plus years of trying to resolve my irregular periods, not a single doctor offered me options other than the birth control pill. If I had relied solely on their advice and beliefs, I would have never found a solution for my reproductive issues, and I strongly believe that I would have had a very hard time getting pregnant later on. We need to listen to our bodies because they are designed to guide us through sensations and emotions in order to show us how to thrive. Sometimes this means investigating further and looking deeper when we are told there is no solution to our condition.

It's important to remember that all practitioners are human and everyone has their own perspective, which may at times be inaccurate. My instinct always told me that there had to be a solution for my period irregularities, but time and time again, this instinct was challenged by what I was hearing from my doctors. I am so glad that I continued searching for a better way because, had I not done that, I don't know where I would be today.

Reproductive health is a reflection of overall health. When anything in our bodies shows us symptoms, such as reproductive challenges, it means that either our bodies are not getting something they need or something is getting in the way of their ability to function optimally. Fertility challenges show that our bodies' natural rhythms and tendency to reproduce have somehow veered off track. While we get discouraged by our symptoms, they are actually really amazing expressions of our bodies' intelligence. If it weren't for symptoms, we wouldn't know how to gauge our bodies' vitality and if what we are doing is working or not. We can think of symptoms like an internal compass that lets us know whether we are getting close to our target of optimal health or moving further away from it. Symptoms are there to provide insight and direction.

My View of the Word "Infertility"

I don't love using the word "infertility" since it feels too decisive and is a label that oftentimes gets proven to be inaccurate. The word "infertility" implies an inability to conceive, when in reality, trouble conceiving may be a temporary condition or a symptom of one's body not being in an optimal state to support fertility. (This is the case for the majority of my patients.) Even if someone is currently having trouble conceiving, that doesn't mean the label "infertile" is accurate to describe their fertility potential, and this label may cause them to feel inadequate and incapable.

Instead, I use "fertility challenges," even in my practice notes. I feel those words more accurately fit my patients' conditions and reflect that I have hope in their bodies' potential to restore their reproductive abilities.

You Are the One

When you are trying to conceive, you play a starring role. Essentially, you are *the one* who creates the bridge to bring life forth. What that means is that, while attention often tends to go to the end goal, the baby, the attention first needs to go to your *self*.

Imagine you are inviting a really important guest over, and you want to make sure everything is in order. The guest needs to be housed, fed, and nurtured. To make that happen, you as the host have to have the capacity to take care of those things. Ultimately, the guest's needs are dependent on the host's wellbeing; if the host's needs aren't met, this will naturally impact the guest as well.

You cannot truly serve the guest without first preparing and helping the host. You first need to figure out what the host needs and make the host happy. As the host, your well-being is essential as you invite new life, yet so many women I've spoken have overlooked this essential step. They leave no stone unturned in their road to starting a family, but they forget that *they are the road*. This means that they need to turn their attention and love toward themselves, filling themselves with love, nurturing, and self-care. Although this may not seem direct, this is one of the ways reproductive health is boosted. Self-care means answering the needs of your body, mind, and spirit. It's listening and paying attention to what your body is communicating with you.

Self-care does not have to just be physical; it could be spending time doing things that elevate your spirit, such as spending quality time with loved ones, reading books, or listening to music. Self-care is about responding to yourself and your needs because they matter when it comes to your fertility.

Julia Didn't Realize She Was the One

Many years ago, I had a patient, Julia, who was going through major trauma trying to conceive her second child after giving birth to her first daughter successfully through IVF. I will never forget that, as her primary complaint, she wrote, "My fertility journey is making me insane."

Julia had the MTHFR (methylenetetrahydrofolate reductase) gene mutation, which makes it difficult for the body to process and absorb folic acid. Since folate is essential for fetal development, this gene mutation can contribute to fertility challenges and can lead to frequent miscarriages.

Julia had gone to many different doctors, nutritionists, and acupuncturists, and she had had multiple IVF cycles. The IVF process is never guaranteed, and it requires preparations such as hormonal injections ahead of both the retrieval and transfer. A full cycle of IVF can take up to a few months.

Many of these attempts had failed, and Julia had ended up with one early miscarriage and then another pregnancy that she had had to terminate at twenty weeks due to severe abnormalities. She was waking up multiple times each night with shortness of breath, and she felt immense stress and trauma from her experiences.

When I first heard her story, my heart broke for Julia. I distinctly remember her saying, "I'm not coming to get treatments for myself; everything I am doing is for my second baby." That was an eye-opening moment for me as a practitioner.

Julia was at her wits' end. At the same time, even as exhausted as she was, Julia did not make it to the top of her own priority list. I explained to Julia that it was herself that she needed to prioritize, even though that might seem like a foreign concept.

At first, this idea didn't make sense to Julia, and while I advocate for self-care, I completely understood why she felt the way she did. When a woman goes through the fertility journey, it can be so traumatic, confusing, and exhausting that she loses her bearings and sense of direction. The last thing she thinks of is self-care; she is just looking for the option that will give her the quickest way through her journey.

Unfortunately, in most cases, there are no shortcuts, and the way to find alignment on your journey is by coming home to yourself. As for Julia, she took a break from her fertility treatments and found a supportive online community as she redirected her goal to nurturing her well-being. I am happy to share that, shortly after Julia began putting herself first, she eventually got pregnant and gave birth to a healthy second baby!

Julia's story is a testament to the importance of self-care and recognizing one's own needs. Sometimes this can look like doing everything you can to support yourself, like receiving acupuncture, eating right, exercising, and meditating. Other times, it can be taking a long break from all things fertility! It's about listening to and honoring what your body and mind are thirsting for. For many, this means putting the brakes on all efforts to get pregnant in order to realign and balance their well-being. One thing for sure is that no one knows better what is best for you than you do, and that is because you have direct access to your body's intelligence and wisdom.

The Power of Alignment

Reclaiming our fertile nature is an invitation to the highest alignment of our bodies, minds, and spirits. Apart from the many other differences between traditional Chinese medicine and conventional medicine, traditional Chinese medicine considers a person's spirit and mind as intricately connected to physical health and vitality. When we can address obstacles that are veering us out of alignment, which is a big focus of traditional Chinese medicine, we facilitate an environment for our bodies to heal and regulate, so they can be primed to procreate.

Your body has an intelligent design that ensures that the body maintains the balance it needs in order to create the harmony necessary for optimal vitality and procreation. One of the ways it does this is through communication. If the body is too hot, hungry, tired, and so on, it will make sure you are so uncomfortable that you will do whatever is necessary to address this discomfort.

So why do people get imbalanced? Many times, this is a result of ignoring those cues, as I shared in my own personal story earlier. People often learn that overworking and ignoring their bodies gets them attention and perhaps success and bonuses at work. By becoming conditioned to those rewards, they bypass their bodies' communication and, instead, rely on external feedback. This shift supports responses that are out of alignment with their bodies' and minds' needs. My hope is that this book will rekindle your body's innate ability to not only reproduce but thrive!

A Note on the Medical Side of Fertility

In order to rule out any underlying medical conditions, such as hormone imbalances, tube blockages, polycystic ovary syndrome (PCOS), and so on, it's important to get baseline tests done by an OB-GYN or reproductive endocrinologist.

This book will not cover medical conditions that could be contributing to fertility challenges or offer medical advice. I encourage all readers to find appropriate healthcare providers who can take part in helping uncover any medical conditions that may be getting in the way. This book is in no way meant to be used as an alternative to medical treatment.

How This Book Is Organized

This book will provide an understanding of the subtle yet powerful ways that you can align your body and life to optimal vitality using ancient wisdom teachings such as Taoism (which traditional Chinese medicine is rooted in). Understanding the basic laws of nature and its wisdom and how to apply these in your daily life can encourage overall wellness and improved reproductive health.

It is my deep desire that this book be a co-creation between you and me where you engage with the prompts throughout this book with a journal. Becoming empowered requires taking ownership of your fertile future by giving yourself a voice, which is why writing your thoughts down and engaging with the exercises is so powerful.

Each chapter in this book builds upon the next, so it's important to read them in order. Before we start, though, I want to personally congratulate you on taking this journey to find out how to activate your reproductive potential—and learn why you're so fabulous and powerful in the process!

My Wish for You

It is my wish that, after reading this book, you have hope, rekindle your innate intuitive gift, and realize that you are more powerful than you can imagine. I hope that you will uncover a deep wealth of wisdom lying dormant within you that can guide you to your greatest dream: having your baby. Ultimately, *you* can feel your body's cues most intimately, and sometimes the best of doctors don't have all the answers. Therefore, it's important for you to develop a strong practice of listening to your body's communication, and the following chapters will cover many ways to do so.

What I encourage you to do before embarking on this journey with me is to write down what you wish to gain on your journey (besides the obvious—having your bundle of joy!). Specifically, how would you feel in your ideal circumstance? Where would you be and what would you be doing? How would your loved ones be affected, and how would that impact your relationship? Be specific and allow yourself to envision not just *getting* there, but *being* there. Pay attention to any resistance that comes up to allowing yourself to entertain your deepest desire of starting or growing your family. If you note resistance, don't let that hold you back from envisioning. All creations start with a vision, so it's important to allow yourself to envision the dream you desire to create.

Last, I want you to go into this reading journey with your mind open to concepts that look different from what you started with. You don't have to believe everything that is being shared, but allow yourself the opportunity to try the concepts on without judgment, and then decide for yourself if they feel right for you.

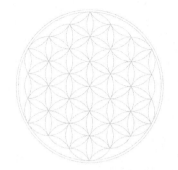

CHAPTER 2

Awareness Is Your Superpower

E very conscious choice you make begins first with awareness. This includes your choice to read this book!

Awareness is not just about perceiving; awareness is, in and of itself, focused, intelligent energy. Wherever you put your energy, you also breathe life. Your attention is like the light of the sun; it allows for clarity but also for growth. Awareness can also bring to light where you are focusing your energy, whether consciously or unconsciously. Awareness allows us to invite in insight so that we can make more effective choices in all areas of our lives.

Taoism teaches that when we let go of false identifications and beliefs, the true nature of reality reveals itself. It's by getting into a state of full presence that we become aware of the Tao, which, it is said, cannot be experienced through words but through our realization of it. Awareness is what sheds light and helps us recognize any false beliefs we hold that are getting in the way of our highest alignment toward vitality, which ultimately reflects in reproductive health.

Sometimes awareness can be uncomfortable, especially when it shows us that changes need to be made in order to get what we are looking for. This is why, in many circumstances, it can be very easy to suppress our awareness. At times, it can feel like looking the other way protects us—but this can actually have an adverse effect. Imagine how safe it would be to walk around with your eyes closed!

We've all had times where we chose to ignore something that didn't feel convenient to address. I can speak for myself that most of the time, I regretted not listening to that awareness after the fact.

Awareness can be looked at as mindfulness in action. When it comes to fertility health, awareness is absolutely key. By cultivating a sense of awareness and paying close attention to your body and its inner workings, you can gain valuable insight into what steps you need to take to optimize your fertility. This is why implementing practices such as cycle charting and noticing how you feel at different points in your cycle can be so powerful.

When you begin to pay attention to your body's cues, you will strengthen your path of communication and may notice that your body communicates with you more.

Becoming aware of what's happening in your body allows you to be proactive about taking the right steps to help it function at its best. Our awareness acts as our guide, lighting our path and showing us where our attention needs to go. When we embrace this as a superpower, we can empower our lives.

Mindfulness Is a Potent Tool

Mindfulness is a powerful tool that can be transformative to those who practice it. Most of us think of meditation when we hear the word "mindfulness." However, mindfulness isn't just reserved for meditation. It's a way of life that can be practiced in every moment. Whether we're eating, walking, or presented with triggering situations, we can bring a mindful presence to our experiences. This can help us become more attuned to our bodies and may even aid in the digestion of food.[1]

The act of becoming mindful, whether it is to our breath, our body sensations, or a repeated mantra, is a way to cue our consciousness to the present moment. When we train our minds to become mindful, it can impact our inflammatory response and even the way our genes express themselves.[2] Mindfulness can also improve sleep quality, which is vital for hormone balance and fertility health.

Training ourselves to become aware of how our bodies feel will help us connect with our intuition. Our bodies usually have instinctual responses that let us know whether something feels aligned or not. This can take the form of what we refer to as a "gut feeling," an inner knowing when something feels off before we can confirm the knowledge. Animals are even more connected with this knowing than we are; for them, it is an instinct of survival (and they don't have the amazing ability to overthink that we do!).

Mindfulness can attune us to our inner wisdom, which can help us make better food and lifestyle choices that will lead us to better fertility health. You can thank your body's intelligent design for this amazing ability. We were designed to know how to heal ourselves way before we had a thing called "doctors." When we understand and acknowledge that our bodies want to survive and procreate, we can also acknowledge that one of the ways they can make that survival possible is by communicating with us.

One of the ways we can gain access to our bodies' intelligence is through something called interoception. Interoception is the ability to tune in to our bodies' sensations and understand what they are trying to tell us. By increasing our awareness of interoception, we gain insight into our bodies' needs and can take steps to heal ourselves. Making this connection between our bodies and minds is a powerful key to promoting self-healing.

When practicing mindfulness meditation, we train our minds to become more in tune with our thoughts and body sensations. By doing this, we create a habit of mindfulness. But, as mentioned earlier, mindfulness is not only done during meditation. It is a practice that we can implement in every aspect of our lives in order to help us align with our bodies' needs. Remember, when we align our bodies to self-heal, we are benefiting our fertility health, as it is a reflection of overall health and balance.

We Feel Emotions throughout the Body

When we feel emotions, we typically get so absorbed in those feelings that we may not realize that they are felt throughout the body. One of the quickest ways to ease the charge of strong emotions is by going into the body and becoming aware of the sensations we are feeling. Our instinct can be to try to resolve emotions from the same state of mind that is experiencing those emotions. Doing so, however, makes it virtually impossible to be objective since our state of mind is resonant with those emotions we want to resolve. In order to get that objectivity, we must first create a space from which awareness can occur. The simplest way to do that is to observe with curiosity our bodies' sensations.

One of the things we can become aware of is our breath. When you begin a practice of observing your breath, you will begin to see a pattern and tendency in response to certain emotions. Again, this can only be done with a consistent practice of awareness. Awareness is the light that shines into our inner terrain. The more we familiarize ourselves with it, the more we can map it out. When we map it out, we become more empowered and less prone to getting triggered.

Familiarizing ourselves with our inner terrain through body sensations also allows us to release old traumas and blocks that are often stored in our bodies. Our initial knee-jerk reaction when faced with uncomfortable emotions is to freeze or constrict. What that does is lock these emotions in our bodies. This is why doing acupuncture, massage, or yoga can bring about a cathartic release of emotions. I have come in so many times at the end of a treatment session to find a patient's face drenched in tears. I always encourage those types of emotional release, as I know they are so vital to the healing process.

Women can hold blocks in their reproductive organs that reflect old trauma that they experienced. Those types of blocks are very hard to uncover because doing so means revisiting or reliving an old traumatic event. Sometimes, simply paying attention to where we feel stuck can trigger a release. It can take time for a release to occur, which is why it's important to make this type of mindful awareness a daily practice so that the body knows it has a safe space in which it can let go. By simply observing with a steady awareness, you are shining a light that encourages release.

How to Implement Mindfulness

As I mentioned earlier, mindful awareness, or mindfulness, is a practice that can be used in every aspect of our lives. Mindfulness is a practice of focusing our awareness at any given moment, and once we focus on something that is happening in the now, that automatically shifts us to the present moment. If you stop and notice, you may begin to realize that it's easy to spend most of your time thinking about things that either happened in the past or will happen in the future. How much time do you find yourself in complete presence of the now moment?

When we engage in our thoughts, we are actually held in an illusory movie that is not based in reality. Yes, your thoughts can be about something that you remember in reality or something that you plan will be reality in the future, but most often, they only exist in the mind. Thoughts aren't bad; they are a necessary part of our minds. It is important to note that most thoughts arise from the brain's negative bias, which is a tendency to worry or expect negative circumstances. This is our brain's way of protecting us in case we need to prepare for or expect the worst. However, this negative bias doesn't always serve us, and it takes us away from the present moment. Our minds can get caught up in thoughts that bring up difficult emotions of defeat. Rarely do these emotions empower us, and they often rob us of necessary energy.

When we invite mindful awareness, we allow a space between our thoughts and the observer. The observer is your consciousness, and when you move into the space of becoming aware of those thoughts, you realize that you are not your thoughts. It is very common to feel identified with your thoughts because they come from your mind. We can even become protective over our thoughts; we often convince ourselves to believe in them or even feel that they *are* us. When we believe in a reality, it can be very jarring to shift that belief. Once we become aware, however, then we realize that who we are is far more vast than a thought, a perception, or a belief. We enter our sacred power by recognizing our true selves from this vantage point. This can only happen with present awareness.

Whether or not you realize it, who you are is way more limitless than your mind-made thoughts can ever identify. Implementing mindfulness can help you connect to this sacred awareness so that you can make more aligned decisions for your fertility treatments and recognize your self-healing potential.

Menstrual Cycle Awareness

Your menstrual cycle offers one of the most profound windows of insight into your reproductive health. When I went to school to study traditional Chinese medicine, we were trained to always ask a woman of menstruating age detailed questions about her menstrual cycle as well as her menses. The menstrual cycle is an umbrella that includes the menses (the bleed) but also refers to the complete cycle from the first day of one period to the next. Awareness of your cycle can reveal many underlying imbalances, and I highly encourage all my patients to chart their basal body temperature (BBT) for at least one month.

BBT charting is a valuable practice for women who want to better understand their menstrual cycle. By taking your temperature daily using a BBT thermometer, you can track your ovulation and gain insight into your body's natural rhythm. You can choose to use a menstrual cycle app or print out a BBT chart. The data collected from charting your BBT can provide essential information about your fertility, helping you plan and optimize your chances of conception. BBT charting provides a comprehensive picture of your menstrual cycle. If you'd like to learn more about how to track your BBT, go to https://www.michelleo ravitz.com/thewayoffertilityresources.

Some women find BBT charting to be a chore or express that it causes them stress. While there are other ways to get insight into one's cycle, including bracelet monitors or even urine testing, nothing compares to doing BBT charting. Using a simple over-the-counter ovulation predicting kit (OPK) won't truly confirm ovulation because all the kits test for is an LH (luteinizing hormone) surge. LH is released from the pituitary gland in the brain to trigger ovulation, but just because it is present doesn't mean ovulation occurred. If you absolutely cannot chart your BBT, then note that the only way to confirm ovulation through urine is to have a strip that also tests for progesterone metabolites.

Measuring BBT can show you whether you are ovulating within a good range or too early/late. An irregular temperature may prompt you to have your thyroid checked (the thyroid supports many important functions in the body, including conception and pregnancy). BBT tracking can also provide acupuncturists with great insight into yin and yang balance or other pattern imbalances.

Besides measuring BBT, I also recommend journaling about how you are feeling at different points of your cycle. This includes noting how your emotions feel, how much energy you have, and whether you feel productive. You can also note physical changes you observe, such as an increase in cervical mucus discharge during your fertile window, or any symptoms you may be feeling during the different phases of your menstrual cycle. After doing this for a few months, you might begin to recognize a pattern. Knowing that on certain days you have more bandwidth for big undertakings than you do on other days can be a tremendous advantage in helping you to strategize about how to allocate your personal energy according to your personal rhythm. This can feel like cracking the code on how to work with your own flow, and it allows you to optimize your reproductive and menstrual cycle energy!

These actions really just come down to increasing awareness of your cycle, but the benefits of empowerment and clarity outweigh the efforts.

Journaling: A Peek inside Our Subconscious Mind

Journaling is hands down one of the best ways to get a peek into your underlying beliefs and the inner workings of your mind. It can be incredibly cathartic, as it allows you to shine a light of awareness onto things that you are holding on to that no longer serve you. Sometimes by simply asking yourself questions in writing and then answering them, you can get great insight and discover pearls of wisdom you never knew existed within you!

Automatic writing works in a similar way. Automatic writing is the practice of writing a question and then allowing yourself to respond without thinking much about what you're writing. When you move out of your inner editor, you allow yourself the freedom to simply express what pops up without judgment. This helps to remove the inner critic, which makes way for you to connect with yourself on a subconscious level. This is where your intuition is able to come into your field of awareness. Our intuition is our soul's conscious awareness, which we often like to dim because it doesn't make sense to our analytical minds.

When you start a journaling practice, you create space for your inner workings to express themselves. Journaling is one of the best forms of self-care and an incredible way to bring awareness into the depth of your being. As mentioned earlier, you can implement journaling to increase awareness and insight into your menstrual cycle. You can also incorporate journaling about how you feel when you eat certain foods. By doing so, you observe what is most aligned with you (and are able to recognize what works against you so that you can eliminate it from your life).

Journaling is also a powerful tool to help you make sense of the many conflicting emotions and thoughts that can arise during the fertility journey. When you acknowledge and write about those thoughts and emotions, they can become easier to mentally digest and release than when they are lingering in the background of your mind. This can bring you clarity and insight into what type of fertility doctor and protocol you are seeking and what options would be best aligned for you and your partner.

A great way to start a journaling practice is by scheduling it in addition to another existing routine. For example, mornings around your tea can be a great time to write, and this is also a great way to clear your thoughts before the day starts. If you feel you're busy, then set an alarm five minutes before you usually wake up and then journal for those five minutes every day! Starting with small changes but consistently repeating them daily is the formula to starting a new habit—it's all about repetition.

If you feel worried that someone will find your journal, then do what I did years ago (around the time my life and menstrual cycle transformed): write in your journal, then rip out the paper and throw it out! I found this to be like taking a weight off my shoulders every time—I literally discarded my worries in the trash!

Awareness Meditation

A meditation practice that invites more conscious awareness trains your mind to become more mindful, even outside of the meditation. When you begin to pay attention to the subtleties of your breath, body sensations, and mind, you illuminate your awareness, and this will ultimately cultivate your personal power. Your attention can also have an impact on your mind–body connection, which can help you influence both your bodily health and your reproductive health over time. Becoming aware of your body's cues can also strengthen your emotional regulation skill when needed.[3]

Below is a meditation practice to help you become aware of what I refer to as your "inner terrain."

Begin by finding a comfortable seated position somewhere you will not be disturbed for at least fifteen to twenty minutes. You can sit either cross-legged or in a chair with your back comfortably erect. Do not lie down, as this can cause your body to fall asleep.

Take a few moments to become aware of your breath. Are you constricting your breathing, or are you breathing freely? Are you breathing shallowly, or are you breathing deeply? Do you notice any tension in your breath?

After paying attention to your breath for a few minutes, begin scanning your body from the top of your head. Pay attention to any tension you might be holding in your scalp. Even if you don't notice any tension, notice what your scalp feels like. Slowly move down into your forehead, then eyes, then ears, cheeks, nose, and mouth. Begin feeling this light of awareness spread through every part of your head and face. Continue down into your throat and neck, becoming aware of the sensations of both your skin and the interior of your throat, including the feeling of each breath traveling through your neck. Move down through the chest as well as the shoulders and arms, then down through your upper, mid, and lower back. Sense the lungs as well, then the abdomen and the digestive and reproductive organs. Really feel those areas. Move down through the pelvis, sacrum, and hips, then down to the front and back of your legs as your awareness travels down to your shins and calves, ankles, feet, and toes.

As you scan your body inside and out, you may feel the urge to stay in certain areas that feel especially tense or stagnant. If you do, that's perfectly okay. You'll find that your awareness is not just observant, but it also has the power to regulate and clear energetic stagnation simply through observation.

Continue as long as it feels right. The more you do this practice, the more you strengthen your body awareness, which can also provide you with an opportunity to improve your overall life force vitality.

Awareness Illuminates Our True Nature

The true gift of awareness is that it can serve as a conduit to our true nature, which is boundless love. Our true nature is one that we know deep within our hearts, but too often it gets overshadowed by the noise of the world. By creating a practice of awareness, you can bring yourself back to your divine truth and uncover the wisdom that has resided within your essence (and always will).

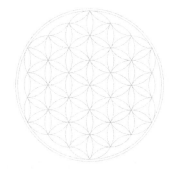

CHAPTER 3

Love and the Fertility Archetype

I n ancient Chinese culture, couples would pray to Guanyin when experiencing challenges starting a family. Guanyin, also referred to as Kuan Yin or Kwan Yin, was revered as the goddess of compassion and fertility. She was believed to bestow the blessings of children, as she was also perceived to be the goddess of mercy. She embodied an essence of the sacred feminine. Her origins are thought to derive from Taoism, which is the origin of Chinese medicine. Guanyin symbolized unconditional love and was seen as a protector of women and children.[1]

If you look throughout history, many cultures have referred to a female deity or energy (Mother Mary, Isis, Aphrodite, Freyja, Shechinah) that symbolizes unconditional love and a source of nurturing. Interestingly, Chinese medicine teaches that there is a connection between the heart and the uterus through the Bao Mai channel and that the heart plays an important role in opening the uterus. I see Guanyin's symbolism to be very applicable to the life-giving energy that love bestows on whatever it touches, and we can draw inspiration from the archetype of Guanyin to approach fertility from a state of love rather than fear.

Guanyin's essence, being that of the sacred feminine, breathes life through love. When we engage in any endeavor from a place of love, we are able to immerse our whole beings into a state of presence and aliveness. Learning from an archetype can be incredibly powerful, as we are hardwired to mirror that which we learn from and see. I have felt Guanyin's essence touch my life in so many ways. I feel her essence inspiring my art and my fertility practice, guiding my intuition as I help my patients and clients navigate their fertility journeys.

In this chapter, I will share how anyone on the fertility journey can benefit from adopting the feminine archetype qualities, which include compassion and love. It is my belief that this is the gift that Guanyin's archetype is showing us, that by embracing unconditional love, we subsequently invite a state of fertility for our bodies and souls.

Love Is Life-Giving

We know that babies cannot survive without love. It is a basic need in all of our lives. Babies that lack sufficient love and physical touch are slower to grow, and their human growth hormone production is slower than that in babies who are given the love they need. Their orbitofrontal cortex, an area of the brain situated behind the eyes that is responsible for the senses of taste and touch, is slower to develop when they lack sufficient human interaction. Research also shows that neglect and other stress early in life can cause alterations to the orbitofrontal cortex.[2] This leads to emotional and health problems throughout life.

In contrast, research also shows that preterm infants who receive at least one hour of increased physical touch per day through skin-to-skin contact showed higher scores on behavioral organization, and their vagal tone matured significantly.[3] Not only did the infants benefit, but their mothers were also less depressed and had a stronger adaptation to their infants' cues. Regular touch for preterm infants has also been shown to reduce health risks associated with premature birth.[4]

It cannot be stressed enough that love is necessary for new life.

Without love, a person can find themselves in severe distress. This is because love is interwoven into the fabric of our essence as human beings. We need to feel a sense of belonging and the security of knowing our importance in the eyes of others. When we feel loved, it naturally enlivens us and affirms our existence through others.

We also have a need to give love, as it gives us a sense of peace and purpose in our own hearts. Even children have a strong pull to cuddle with loved ones or animals; there is a feeling of security and warmth in making this divine connection that feels eternal and timeless.

The natural draw that we have toward love should not be ignored when it comes to fertility health. If children need love after they're born, what makes us think they don't need it to encourage their conception? Yet, when couples feel stressed and become hyper-focused on the end goal, conception, it can be very easy to become so emotionally depleted that nurturing this necessary state can be forgotten. This is unfortunate, as the fertility journey doesn't just *benefit* from love; it actually *depends on* being sustained with love to increase its chances of success.

Love breathes life into everything it touches. Stories throughout the ages have shared the impacts that love has on people's lives. Even creative people often tap into deeply profound emotion as a means to translate their souls' conceptions. Our attention, when focused with the charge of love, begins to take on an unmatched force. Love is a motivation that calls people to move mountains. It imbues the sweet fragrance of meaning into our choices and actions. It is not by accident that a higher soul connection between lovers leads to new life. We don't necessarily need love in order to procreate, but when we do have a foundation of love, it sets a solid foundation for a more cohesive and supportive unit on which life can thrive!

I invite you to think of love as the fuel that will help you on your fertility journey. Love will make every step feel more hopeful, and it will invite more trust in the process. By embracing a sense of love, you are not denying any sadness that arises. By contrast, you will immerse yourself in compassion, allowing and validating your feelings as they come up. Allowing yourself to feel is what will free you from a state of constant suffering so that you can navigate your journey with more clarity and ease.

Closing Ourselves Off to Love Gives Us a False Sense of Safety

You may have had moments in your life when you were angry with a person or a situation. Your response may have been to close up in retaliation. Sometimes, closing up makes you feel strong and solid, as if you have armor that can keep all the things you don't want in your life away. While this can be a safety mechanism at times, that sense of safety can be misleading. We may feel that closing up in this way is necessary so that we can protect ourselves (and sometimes that's true!); however, this can turn into a habitual response that is unnecessary and can prevent us from being in a state of giving and receiving love.

As humans, we have natural tendencies and responses—like protecting ourselves—that are there for a reason. But many of these tendencies are not meant to stay chronic. When they do, they can cause us to have an imbalance in our relationship to life events. Emotions are moving, and they need to be allowed to flow. If they stay too long, this may be a sign that we are holding them in place through either attachment or resistance. Resistance keeps things in place, and attachment can actually push things away. A state of allowing can help us move through discomfort so that it doesn't stagnate and build up.

Many of my patients have expressed to me that the stress of having fertility challenges has evoked a feeling of anger toward their bodies. This can be very normal, as they are processing the contrast between their current circumstances and their initial expectations of conceiving. After their natural response, I often work with them on encouraging reconnection and compassion toward themselves and their bodies. This may seem like a strange thing to introduce, especially when one is experiencing so much disappointment and what feels like an uphill battle. But cutting oneself off from love is not the answer.

Naturally cultivating that self-compassion takes time. Part of self-compassion is understanding your feelings and allowing yourself to feel them without judgment. It is also important to acknowledge that you are where you need to be and that there is no right or wrong way to process your experience.

Forgiveness Opens Our Hearts

Forgiveness is a powerful tool that can bring about healing and open us up to love. When we hold on to grudges and resentment, they can weigh heavily on our hearts and prevent us from experiencing the fullness of our love for life. Holding on to anger can also lead to detrimental health impacts such as coronary heart disease.[5] I find it interesting how closing our hearts to love on an emotional level can have a direct effect on our physical hearts.

Forgiveness allows us to free ourselves from the heavy weight of anger and resentment, and it opens our hearts to compassion and love. Research has shown that the act of forgiveness can have a profound impact on our physical and emotional well-being, reducing stress and promoting a sense of inner calm.[6] In episode 71 of *The Wholesome Fertility Podcast*, where I spoke to Qi Gong master Chunyi Lin, Master Lin shares how he healed his body of severe arthritis by adopting a Qi Gong practice and beginning to practice forgiveness. In Master Lin's first Qi Gong retreat, his teacher prompted him to forgive any person who had caused him harm. At first, he had a hard time with this, so his teacher suggested that he say, "I pretend to forgive you," while bringing up images in his mind of those who had caused him harm. Master Lin mentioned that forgiveness can be profoundly therapeutic and was a vital aspect of his own healing process; his arthritis resolved after he completed the forgiveness exercise. Master Lin describes healing as something that is not only physical but spiritual as well, and forgiveness plays a powerful role in the healing process.[7]

It's important to note that when we forgive others, that does not mean we condone their actions or excuse their behavior. Rather, we are choosing to let go of our negative emotions and release the hold that the past has on us. There is a common misconception that holding on to a grudge makes us strong and will punish those who have hurt us. Instead, it creates a weight for us to carry that absorbs our mental and physical life force. Forgiveness is not always the easiest process to go through, but it can become a catalyst for removing a huge burden of density in our lives. It allows us to move forward with a lighter heart and a greater capacity for love. It can truly be a medicinal practice.

Forgiveness is not just about letting go of our anger toward others; we also need to forgive ourselves. When we hold on to the guilt and shame that may arise on the fertility journey, it can hold us back from our most authentic expression. It creates a feeling of unworthiness where we don't feel deserving of receiving our deepest desire: conceiving a child. This can become a vicious cycle. So what can disrupt this cycle of shame? Forgiveness and grace.

In order to truly forgive, it is helpful to start by accepting "what is," even if it doesn't meet our initial expectations. This alone can bring a huge sense of emotional liberation and release. Acceptance requires trust, courage, and vulnerability. As scary as that may initially feel, forgiveness will ultimately bring you more personal power than staying locked in a state of resentment would. By releasing this resentment, you are allowing the transformative power of love to flow through your heart unimpeded!

Coming from a Place of Self-Love: Why We Are Conditioned Not to Love Ourselves

Just like we need to give and receive love, we also need self-love. Yet so many of us struggle to love ourselves. There seems to be a stigma to self-love; self-love can be seen as selfish, and this can lead us to dim our light to make others feel more comfortable. This underlying belief that self-love is selfish can exist without us even realizing it and can have a lasting impact on our self-esteem and self-worth.

Fear of judgment from others can also be a significant factor in why we struggle to love ourselves. We are often told to conform to societal norms, to fit in, and to be like everyone else. But this kind of thinking can be harmful to our mental health and well-being. We become so focused on pleasing others that we forget to check in with ourselves. We may even feel guilty for doing things that bring us joy, thinking that we are being selfish. In the end, this becomes self-punishment, which, by its nature, is not conducive to a healthy way of living.

Another thing that gets in the way of self-love is comparison. For many women, feelings of comparison begin at an early age; it's not uncommon to feel that you must look like the photoshopped models on magazine covers to be "worthy" of love. We are bombarded with edited, curated social media posts that purposefully capture single, beautifully selected moments in the posters' subjects' lives. Women who are experiencing challenges conceiving can feel tremendous defeat when seeing pregnancy announcements and gender reveal posts. This creates a sense of unworthiness that makes it hard *not* to compare. We may focus on what we're missing instead of celebrating how far we've come. This kind of negative self-talk can make it harder to navigate the already challenging journey of trying to conceive.

It's important to recognize that a lot of negative self-talk is habitual. When we acknowledge this, we can implement new habits in the way we speak to ourselves. We can learn to see our imperfections with more compassion and grace, looking at ourselves the same way we do our loved ones. With cultivation and time, self-love can grow into a boundless life force that nourishes our emotional and reproductive health. Take moments throughout each day to remind yourself to practice self-compassion and love; this may feel foreign at first, but remember that when you focus your love, you are focusing your innate healing energy. By focusing this energy on yourself, you are opening yourself up to healing vitality that will synchronistically impact your fertility health.

Even though this practice may seem strange at first, I see many of my patients who try it coming to a place of surrendering to self-love. I believe that being in a state of self-love is our true essence, and it's about shedding false beliefs about ourselves and realizing just how magnificent and worthy of love we really are. Realize that shining love to yourself is shining love to your future baby—your baby comes to and through your beautiful vessel of love!

How Learning to Love Herself Transformed Her Fertility Journey

Allie was a podcast listener who enrolled in my signature program, The Wholesome Fertility Method online program. Allie shared with me that she experienced a self-imposed pressure to be "perfect." She was a successful fitness trainer, and she thought that she needed to look a certain way in order to succeed. She had suffered from an eating disorder for many years and had sought professional help, going through years of back and forth to find a balance. But even though she was in recovery, Allie was stressed and struggling with fertility because she hadn't had a period for nine years.

As soon as I heard Allie's story, I felt so much compassion for what she had been through as a woman. I myself have had moments—as have many other women—of wanting to be perfect and fit an unrealistic ideal. This kind of rejection of oneself brings about so much torment and takes people away from living fully. When she came to me, Allie was in a state where a part of her wanted so badly to heal, and she was called by the most powerful motivation of all: her yearning to start a family.

Allie may have had (this is not a diagnosis) hypothalamic amenorrhea, which is a condition that causes a woman's period to stop due to a deficit of calories and/or too much exercise. But, shortly after joining The Wholesome Fertility Method online program, where I outline the importance of supporting fertility with proper nutrition and self-love, Allie fell pregnant and wrote me an email with the subject line "It worked!"

Allie had realized that depriving herself of rest and demanding too much of her body was impacting her body's ability to regulate its menstrual cycle. When she focused on tuning in to what her body needed and providing herself the nourishment she deserved, her body responded!

I can't express how happy I was, not just at the news that Allie was pregnant but that she had nursed herself back to balance and begun to care for herself again.

Allie was happy to share her story with others who may be experiencing challenges like her own. You can hear her story on episode 119 of *The Wholesome Fertility Podcast*.[8] Today, Allie has two kids. She sent me updates throughout her journey, and I thoroughly loved hearing them! Her story is truly one of hope and inspiration.

Loving the Union That Brings Forth Life

So often, I hear my patients and clients share how difficult it is to place meaning into the intimate moments they have with their partners. When dealing with fertility challenges, sex often becomes a chore, devoid of pleasure or connection. Their physical connection becomes diminished as they begin thinking of intimacy as a means to an end. This is so unfortunate, and what is more unfortunate is that couples begin to believe that this change is inevitable. I want to remind you—as I do my clients—that this is not inevitable. You absolutely have a choice, and even if these problems are already coming up for you, you can shift your perspective on them. Not only will reconnecting with your partner make the fertility journey easier to manage, but it will also improve your chances of conceiving!

There is actually a reason why making love creates a cascade of events that leads to the release of emotions, hormones, and bodily fluids. When women are aroused and immersed in their connection with their partners, their level of oxytocin (aka the love hormone) rises, and they secrete vaginal fluid to help support making babies. This creates a catch-22: in order to gain this benefit and be more fertile, couples need to be completely surrendered in the moment. And to be completely surrendered in the moment, both partners need to forget about baby making.

Consider how an orgasm (which also increases oxytocin) is an event that needs full surrender, so much so that a person loses all control when they are consumed by the euphoria that takes place. I believe our bodies are not only super intelligent in their design and function, but they also show us metaphors for what they need from us in order to function best. In regard to baby making, the surrendering and full trust one feels when making love may be the lesson our bodies are trying to show us as a way to conception.

If you find your intimacy with your partner is suffering because of your fertility challenges, you are not alone, and taking matters back into your own hands requires proactive steps. I am a firm believer that when life creates an uphill battle, you need to arm yourself with extra tools so that your climb is successful.

When you're faced with more challenges, then it's time to be more proactive.

Think outside your default response to your partner. By this, I mean take extra time to connect with your partner *outside* of the bedroom. Become intimate *outside* of your fertile window. Go *outside* of your comfort zone to create special moments and surprises for your partner. Improving your chances of starting a family isn't the only benefit of connecting. You will be starting the foundation of your family from a place of love rather than using the union to reach a goal.

Think for a moment about just how much more meaning infusing love brings into creating life. It makes the difference between just going through the motions and operating with soul and purpose.

Suggested Exercise You Can Do with Your Partner

Write down a list of things that made you fall in love with your partner, and have your partner do the same. During this exercise, put temporary blinders on about anything that bothers you about your partner; only focus on their positive attributes.

When you both make your lists, do so alone rather than next to each other. This will allow you and your partner a moment where you can genuinely bring yourselves back to the time and space where you each knew that the other was your person.

As you write your list, focus on the area around your heart. You may start to feel warmth there as you bring yourself back to the love you have for your partner. Here are some prompts you can both use.

Go back to the moment you realized this was someone you wanted to share life with and ask yourself . . .

- *What emotions were you feeling in that moment?*
- *What was it about your partner that brought up those emotions?*
- *What were the things you were most grateful for in your partner?*
- *Was there something unique about your partner that made them different from everyone you had ever met before?*

Take your time writing your list, and set a date to come together with your partner to share your lists with one another. This is a beautiful way to express your love and to provide words to affirm what your partner means to you. Those affirming words work just as powerfully on you as they do on your partner— because they serve as reminders of how your connection started, and they can rekindle the spark that may have been put on hold due to the fertility journey.

Infusing Love and Gratitude for Your Fertility Journey despite its Challenges

I want to conclude with a few more thoughts on why love (and gratitude) can feed your fertility journey and ease your load.

When you love someone, you love them in their entirety. You choose to overlook their flaws because your love for them and the meaning they hold in your life outweigh any of the person's imperfections. You're even willing to put up with the challenges of the relationship because the relationship is worth fighting for. This is the power of love; it infuses any difficulty with more strength than you knew you had.

I would like to propose a similar perspective on your fertility journey. Given that your fertility journey is something you are willing to put up with because of the love you have for your future baby—and make no mistake, that love is real, even if your baby hasn't arrived!—it is a road that you chose to take due to love. Taking a moment to reflect on that can shift the perspective from one of going through the motions to one that is infused with purpose and meaning.

I know that right now it may be hard to imagine feeling this way, but of the hundreds of podcast guests and countless patients and clients I have spoken to, many of whom experienced years of struggle in starting their families, almost all of them now say that they are grateful for what they learned on their journeys. They also say they wouldn't change a thing! Yes, they say that at the beginning they would be angry if anyone even suggested that their journeys would actually help them in the future, but now they see their experiences in a completely different light. And such is the pattern of life; we see things more clearly looking back, while in the present, the unknown is something we want to avoid at all costs.

Infusing love and gratitude into your life during challenging times is the single most powerful practice you can partake in. I say this not to minimize the difficulty or pain that you might be experiencing. I say it because pain, love, and gratitude can exist simultaneously. The love and gratitude are there to assist you, not to invalidate you. They are there to ease your pain, even if they don't take it away entirely. You deserve to feel love, regardless of what is happening in your life right now. Love is your birthright, and it is a sacred gift that you can claim at any moment you choose to.

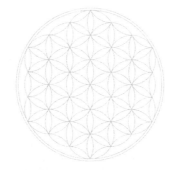

CHAPTER 4

The Wisdom of Yin and Yang

The yin and yang are a representation of the balance and harmony between opposites in nature. This ancient Chinese concept describes the duality and interdependence of all things in the universe. Yin represents the feminine, passive, and dark aspects of nature, while yang represents the masculine, active, and light aspects. The two are not in opposition, but rather are complementary forces that create a whole.

These two contrasting forces support each other while also keeping each other in check. When yin and yang become imbalanced, disease occurs; when they separate, death occurs. Life as we know it here on Earth requires the union of the yin and yang for continuity, as it cannot be sustained without this balance.

The concept of the yin and yang can be applied to all living things in nature. All yin contains a little yang, and all yang contains a little yin. Yin and yang dance in a coordinated and reciprocal fashion. This balance can be seen in everything from the seasons to the human body. For example, winter is a yin season, characterized by darkness and stillness, while summer is a yang season, characterized by light and activity. In the human body, yin and yang correspond to different organs and functions that work interdependently. While each force has its own roles, they complement and influence one another.

Yin and yang are not just limited to physical elements. Their qualities also extend into the realm of emotions and spirituality. To experience inner peace and harmony, we must balance the yin and yang within ourselves. This can be achieved through practices such as meditation, tai chi, Qi Gong, yoga, pranayama, and acupuncture, all of which aim to balance the body's energy flow. Each opposite has a time and a place. Being active and productive can be followed by restorative rest; each helps the other fulfill their objective.

The yin and yang have many practical applications in daily life. For example, in traditional Chinese medicine, we use this concept to diagnose and treat illness. We are trained that restoring balance to the body's yin and yang energies can promote healing and improve overall health. In martial arts, practitioners use the balance of yin and yang to achieve optimal performance and to avoid injury.

In conventional medicine, you may have heard this same yin and yang harmony referred to as "homeostasis." Without homeostasis, our bodies would not be able to function properly, and our health would be at risk. Hormones are one of the main mechanisms that help us achieve homeostasis. These chemical messengers play a vital role in regulating various processes in our bodies, such as metabolism, growth, and reproduction. Hormones help to balance the levels of different substances in our bodies, such as glucose, electrolytes, and water, to ensure that we stay healthy.

If you look at the yin and yang symbol, it depicts that basic formula for life. It has been referred to as the "Diagram of the Great Ultimate," and the concept has been around since approximately 1300 BCE. Although the symbol was created way before we could look at a sperm and egg under a microscope, we can see that it clearly resembles the sperm and egg, the male and female essence. This representation clearly teaches us that reproduction, or new life, requires balance in order to be sustained. Our reproductive health depends on balance in so many ways. The balance of hormones is sustained by our bodies' internal thermostat—it stops production when it senses hormone levels rise and increases production when it is signaled that there is a need for more. We are designed with a delicate yet intelligent system that always seeks harmony.

The yin and yang are the ultimate emblem of Taoism. The wisdom that it teaches us can also be seen as a formula for the creation of flow and vitality, not just in our physical bodies but in all areas of our lives. Once we become mindful of the yin and yang, we are naturally awakened to the gifts that this concept provides us. Ultimately, this awakening is more of a remembering of our nature than a learning of a new concept. Our bodies and minds have been designed with this formula of homeostasis, and therefore, we innately understand it.

In essence, the yin and yang are the basis of all living things because they represent the fundamental balance and interdependence of all aspects of nature. Without this balance, there would be chaos and disharmony. As individuals, we can achieve harmony by embracing both our yin and yang aspects. This not only supports our overall lives, but it also enhances our reproductive health and needs.

What Causes Yin and Yang Disharmony?

When yin and yang energies are in balance, we experience health and vitality. However, when there is a disproportion between them, it causes dis-ease in our bodies, minds, and spirits. There are many factors that can cause our bodies to fall out of their natural balance.

One of the main causes of yin and yang disharmony is our conditioned learning to ignore our bodies' cues. Our bodies are constantly sending us signals and messages about what they need, but we often ignore those signals and push ourselves beyond our limits. We have been conditioned to ignore these cues because we have been taught that hard work is what helps us advance in our jobs and have embraced the "no pain, no gain" concept in place of the harmonious yin and yang concept. For example, we may stay up late to finish a project, skip meals to meet a deadline, or push ourselves to exercise even when we're exhausted. These actions create an imbalance in our energy and disrupt the natural flow of yin and yang.

Eating low-vibrational processed foods, getting inconsistent rest, and having a stressful lifestyle also play a significant role in creating disharmony in our bodies and hormones. Consuming too many yin or yang foods can create an imbalance in our energy. For example, eating too many cold, raw, or sweet foods can lead to an excess of yin energy, while eating too many spicy, fried, or salty foods can lead to an excess of yang energy. Similarly, engaging in a stressful lifestyle or not getting enough rest can disrupt our bodies' natural balance, while living a stagnant, sedentary life can create a clogging of our life force energy.

Living against the way of the Tao creates disharmony in our bodies. The Tao represents the natural flow of life and always adheres to balance and harmony. When we go against the way of the Tao, we disrupt the natural flow of our vitality, which is also responsible for self-healing and self-regulation. Having the prolonged stress and tension that arises from living in disharmony with the Tao can cause energetic stagnation and disrupt the natural flow of yin and yang balance. In addition, our overall ability to achieve our natural homeostasis is compromised when we live against the laws of nature. In other words, by living an unbalanced life, we are making it harder for our bodies and minds to get back into our natural state of vitality, and this will almost always reflect in our reproductive health.

To get back to optimal health, we need to listen to our bodies' cues and live in harmony with the Tao. Remember, we are designed to find our way back to harmony. Being mindful and aware of how your body feels, what causes it to sense disharmony, and when it feels its best are important steps toward restoring harmony.

The More the Arrow Gets Pulled Back, the Stronger Its Force

If you begin thinking in terms of yin and yang, you may notice that our modern life is very yang. Yang energy is depicted as fast-moving, active, restless, and masculine, and it can burn itself out if it isn't equalized by sufficient yin. Does that sound familiar? Just look around you. So many working people may find themselves "burning out" as they push themselves to the limits. What's worse is that taking the necessary time to rest is perceived as laziness or is looked down upon. So many people have become conditioned to feel guilty for taking much-needed rest.

This rest is yin. Yin energy brings us back into our inert shell so that we can restore ourselves to our original state as we anchor the strong yang dominance. By providing ourselves time to retract, we allow ourselves to be like a wave, moving back in order to harness force to move forward. A great example of how yin is needed to create energy is sleep. When you look at someone who is sleeping, it looks like the person is doing absolutely nothing. But remember, yang is able to acquire its fuel as the yin is restored because the two forces are codependent, and each needs the other to exist. The body is busy replenishing and restoring its battery while it sleeps, and so much is happening behind the scenes! In essence, while yin may be seen as inert potential energy, it is also very productive!

Meditation is a powerful yin practice. Similar to when a person is sleeping, a person who is meditating looks like they are doing absolutely nothing. But so much is happening behind the scenes, and a powerful rewiring and reorganizing of energies is allowed to occur. I say "allowed to occur" because when we enter a yin state, we allow and invite rather than run after—and, in turn, lose—more energy. Meditation provides a type of energy that cannot be attained with sleep. It allows the mind and body to naturally realign to their innate harmony.

Energy is vital for sustaining reproduction. Egg cells have hundreds of thousands of mitochondria (which produce energy) compared with just thousands in other cells in the body. This is because a great deal of energy is needed to create another being and to support this miraculous life for nine-plus months. Thus, restoring your energy should be your top priority when trying to conceive. Moving from a state of doing (yang) to a state of being (yin) is a perspective that needs to be embraced in order to balance out the natural stressors of the fertility journey.

Egg Is Yin and Sperm Is Yang

As we discussed earlier, the egg and the sperm are the ultimate symbol of yin and yang—complementary opposites that come together to create a vibrant whole. Both have their distinct characteristics and roles to play in the process of fertilization. The egg is a stable source of potential, while the sperm provides the necessary motility and speed to accomplish their union. Together, they are the foundation from which life emerges.

The sperm, being from the male (which is yang), moves rapidly and has a go-getter energy. It can't get its work accomplished without moving. It also needs lots of stamina to travel a far distance, so it has an abundance of energy! Even though we've established that the sperm is a symbol of yang, it also needs yin so that it can survive and move. It is surrounded by protective fluid, which is very yin (moist). It needs this yin aspect to do its job.

The egg, on the other hand, which happens to be the largest cell in the body, is very yin. The egg represents receptive, nurturing, and containing qualities. Its only movement after ovulation and prior to fertilization is traveling down the fallopian tube, yet it does so in a very stable manner. It remains a calm force, waiting for the right sperm to reach it. The egg also has a large number of yang qualities; it provides the majority of the mitochondria in the zygote (the fertilized egg), giving it the energy it needs to divide and grow. This is why mitochondrial DNA is passed down from the mother to her offspring.

Both egg and sperm can teach us so much! They show us that there is a time to take charge and go after what you want, and there's also a time to call in what you want while remaining still. I love the saying "be the egg"; it describes moving from a state of chasing to a state of attracting and allowing. There is much power in this wisdom of engaging both energies when necessary in life. We not only need both, but we also need to use our discernment to determine when it is appropriate to tune in to one or the other to achieve harmony.

The Yin and Yang in the Menstrual Cycle

As discussed earlier, the yin and yang make their appearance in all of nature, and this includes the menstrual cycle! The menstrual cycle has four phases, which move beautifully into one another and repeat monthly.

The menstrual cycle, being the heartbeat of fertility, reflects so much on the balance a woman has when it comes to her reproductive health. After the menstrual bleed, during the follicular phase, the body's estrogen (estrogen is a yin hormone) levels rise as it works to increase the blood of its lining (blood is a yin substance). This is also a time when cervical mucus increases (mucus, being moist, is a yin substance), and the body is preparing for its "full moon" ovulation phase as it raises its internal tide (cervical fluid). After ovulation, the egg gets released from the follicle, and the menstrual cycle moves into the luteal phase. The temperature drops before it increases (kind of like a heartbeat pattern!) and then stays elevated during the luteal phase (a yang time of the menstrual cycle).

The corpus luteum releases progesterone (a more yang hormone), which is responsible for the temperature increase. "Corpus luteum" translates as "yellow body," and it gets its color from beta-carotene, which is a supplement I often recommend to women who have a short luteal phase.[1] Interestingly, some yellow and orange vegetables that have a warming yang nature, such as carrots, pumpkins, and yams, are high in beta-carotene!

It is really beautiful to witness the yin and yang dance during the menstrual cycle, and this is something that cannot be unseen once you have learned about it! This knowledge can also make it less stressful to do cycle charting since it adds another layer of understanding of the menstrual cycle.

Lessons from the Yin and Yang

The yin and yang teach us that all of life seeks harmony in order to thrive. They give us a formula to look to in order to restore our bodies to a state of self-healing. I often emphasize that with traditional Chinese medicine, practitioners are not the ones who do the healing; it is the body that does the healing. All we do as practitioners is create an environment that is conducive to healing. That environment is a balance of the elements. If there is too much cold, we increase heat. If there is too much stagnation from stress, we move energy and calm the mind.

The lessons of yin and yang apply to every aspect of our lives, including reproduction, our minds, our health, and our relationships. In terms of fertility, the balance between yin and yang is essential for creating new life. The feminine yin energy is necessary for nurturing and supporting the growth of the fetus, while the masculine yang energy provides the necessary drive and initiative for conception. And there is a lot more interplay between yin and yang throughout the process of conception, growth, and birth.

The wisdom of the yin and yang shows us we can be active participants in our health by choosing to live a life that is harmonious. It is not only about eating the right foods and getting proper rest; it is also about the actions, words, and thoughts we choose to repeat. An essential step in supporting our overall health and therefore our reproductive health is embracing harmony in our lives.

Finding Balance

When Emily, a patient of mine who had a very demanding job, first came to me, she put down in her intake form that she had nine out of ten energy (ten being the highest). Yet she was living a very imbalanced life and wasn't sleeping through the night. You don't need to be trained in traditional Chinese medicine to realize that her energy was not "real energy" and that she was operating on overdrive to function in her life.

Emily's period was irregular, and her eating schedule and way of life were also very irregular. She would eat fast food in her car in between meetings, and she felt like she didn't have time to exercise.

Based on her habits and symptoms, I wasn't sure how quickly she would respond to my treatments, but surprisingly, she responded to them immediately. She also took my suggestion to meditate in the morning before she started her day and at night before she went to sleep.

Emily began sleeping so well that her husband was worried she would miss work. She was able to sleep so well because, when the body is trying to balance from too much yang or too much activity, it will need to compensate to the opposite extreme first before it finds a balanced state. So she went from extreme yang to extreme yin and slept deeper with longer hours for almost a month! She shared that she was starting to find that it took her less time to get certain tasks done because her focus felt so much stronger. She also naturally began to crave healthier foods as she awoke her innate sense of seeking healthier choices by listening to her body.

After a few months, Emily began to feel calm and balanced energy. Her menstrual cycle began to regulate, and to her surprise, she got pregnant five months into her treatments. This is a great example of how the body, when it is given the opportunity and resources, wants to pull itself back into balance. It also shows how these changes are not an overnight thing. It takes patience to see results—but it is so worth it!

Yin and Yang Balancing Exercise

Just as I suggested to Emily, meditating in the morning and at night allows time and space to connect with the yin and yang of your day. If you feel that you're especially out of balance, I suggest that you practice the following meditation and breath technique to align the yin and yang aspects of your body and life.

Every morning and every evening, sit in a comfortable position and focus on your breath for a minute or two without changing anything. Simply observe.

After completing the initial step, exhale fully and then cover your left nostril with your finger, inhaling and then exhaling from your right nostril. Then cover your right nostril, inhaling and then exhaling from your left nostril. Continue this alternate nostril breathing technique for about five minutes.

Then go back to observing your breath as it goes in and out for a few minutes. Begin shifting your focus to the space between the breaths—between the inhale and exhale and between the exhale and inhale. You'll notice that the time between the inhale and exhale may be shorter than the time between the exhale and inhale.

Don't change anything about your breath; breathe naturally and simply neutrally observe those points in your breath. These points are like the north and south poles of your breath, and your focus will naturally become more refined with practice. By focusing on these areas, you will naturally be focusing on two opposing parts of your breath in real time.

Doing this twice a day is a very powerful exercise.

Why Everyone Needs to Make Balance a Priority

If the sun (yang) were out endlessly, plants would dry out and life wouldn't be able to sustain itself. Luckily, we have a balance between light and dark so that nature can ebb and flow in order to provide necessary change and a variety of elements. Clearly, we can't go without sun (yang), but we also need water (yin) to get the most of the light provided by nature. Yin and yang are the perfect pair, and they need one another to help each other carry out their purpose.

The yin and yang are not confined to just our bodies or to nature. They expand into every aspect of our lives. They serve as guides to let us know where we have strayed from our ideal path to vitality. The way that we conduct our lives and even the way that our minds function uses both yin and yang. We can see whether we are favoring one over the other, and this can guide us to make changes in order to invite more harmony into our lives. We can apply the concept of yin and yang to diet, exercise, emotions, thoughts . . . virtually anything we can think of!

Traditional Chinese medicine teaches that our kidneys, which hold the energy of reproductive health, also have a yin and yang aspect. Balancing those energies is vital for reproductive energy. We need balance in all areas, and luckily, we have been designed to intuitively know what feels out of balance. Our emotions and states of being are some of the best barometers to signal when we are in or out of balance.

The good news is that, once you become aware of the yin and yang, you will become awakened to your natural tendencies to seek this balance. Getting still is often the best way to revert to your natural state of harmony. Awareness by itself is also one of the most powerful tools of insight you can use, and it can guide you to what you need to harmonize. The body's self-healing tendencies can be awakened fairly quickly once we establish a consistently balanced lifestyle, which includes not only physiological choices such as diet, exercise, rest, and supplements but also mental and emotional choices like supporting a healthy mindset in order to encourage overall balance. Remember, you were designed to already know this; all you need to do is listen to that inner knowing.

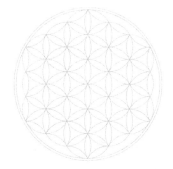

CHAPTER 5
Following the Mother Ship

Nature Is Our Guide

Traditional Chinese medicine teaches that all parts contain the whole. Our bodies are walking, functioning ecosystems that are hardwired to entrain with the rhythms of nature. This is why we feel so off when traveling to time zones that our bodies aren't used to. We are meant to synchronize with nature as it is an incredible guide for our bodies, helping us to find balance, healing, and vitality. We are designed from the same blueprint that designed all of nature. Through its sacred geometry and intricate design, nature can help our bodies align to its rhythms and can support reproductive health. The natural world is abundant with healing properties that can help us feel rejuvenated, refreshed, and balanced.

When we spend time in nature, we allow our bodies to align with nature's rhythms, which can have a profound effect on our overall health and well-being. As mentioned in previous chapters, our reproductive health responds to the balance and vitality of our overall health. Nature's design is also reflected in the intricate workings of our bodies. Our reproductive systems in particular are closely linked to nature's cycles. Nature is inherently fertile, always growing and seeking to thrive. You can tap into this essence to support your own fertility health.

Our bodies blossom when we are in balance, and nature is the perfect place to find this balance, whether we're experiencing the fresh air, the calming sounds of the forest, or the gentle movement of the ocean.

In addition to providing balance, nature is also incredibly healing for the body. Being surrounded by natural beauty can reduce stress, lower blood pressure, improve heart rate variability, and regulate the autonomic nervous system, all of which can support reproductive health.[1] The natural world has an abundance of negative ions, which are oxygen atoms with more negatively charged electrons than those indoors. Negative ions induce a sense of calm and ease while also providing a host of health benefits. Negative ions help improve sleep,[2] reduce headaches,[3] reduce blood pressure,[4] and improve overall mood.[5]

Nature also contains elements that can help to boost our qi, which is essential for reproductive health. When we spend time in nature, we are exposed to fresh air, sunlight, and natural beauty, all of which can help to boost our energy levels, support our circadian rhythm, and improve our overall sense of wellbeing.

That Which Is Not of Nature: Artificial Light, EMFs, and Endocrine Disruptors

Now that you have a better understanding of why we need nature, let's discuss how moving away from nature by using man-made creations can disrupt our natural rhythms. Since our bodies are programmed to regulate by nature's rhythms (a genius design!), they can easily be confused when they encounter similar signals that do not come from nature. These signals include artificial light, EMFs, endocrine disruptors, and more.

Artificial light has become an essential part of our daily lives, but this comes at a cost. Artificial light can affect the production of hormones, which play a crucial role in our overall health.[6] The menstrual cycle, for instance, is regulated by hormones and is closely tied to circadian rhythm,[7] and any disruption to this cycle can lead to health issues.

Circadian rhythm is an essential part of the body's internal clock, which keeps us in sync with the natural patterns of the world around us. When we're exposed to artificial light outside of natural light hours, our bodies' internal clocks become confused and disrupted, leading to a variety of health problems. When we are exposed to too much artificial light, particularly in the evening, our melatonin levels can be disrupted, leading to hormonal imbalances and potential reproductive issues.[8] It's crucial to limit our exposure to artificial light, especially during the night, to help maintain our circadian rhythm and keep our bodies in sync. By doing so, we can promote better sleep and ensure that we keep an aligned rhythm with nature's daily cycle.

Artificial light isn't the only modern technology that may pose a concern to our health. EMFs, or electromagnetic fields, are invisible waves of energy that are emitted by electronic devices such as mobile phones, laptops, and Wi-Fi routers. While EMFs are an essential part of modern technology, there is growing concern about the potential impact of EMF radiation on our health.

Studies have shown that exposure to EMF radiation can have a negative impact on our hormones and reproductive health.[9] For men, EMF radiation can have a detrimental effect on sperm count and quality. This is because radiation can damage the DNA in sperm cells, leading to a decrease in fertility.[10] In women, exposure to EMF radiation can disrupt the hormonal balance, which can impact the menstrual cycle and fertility.[11] Additionally, high levels of EMF radiation can lead to miscarriage and other pregnancy complications.[12]

In addition to its impacts on reproductive health, EMF radiation can also impact our sleep quality. This is because exposure to EMF radiation can disrupt the production of melatonin, a hormone that regulates sleep. This can lead to insomnia, fatigue, and other sleep-related problems.[13] As discussed before, circadian disruption can impact the menstrual cycle as well.

It's important to take steps to reduce our exposure to EMF radiation. This can include using devices that emit lower levels of radiation, such as wired earphones instead of Bluetooth and Wi-Fi. Additionally, limiting our use of electronic devices before bedtime can help reduce the impact of EMF radiation on our sleep. I also like shungite, which is a stone that is thought to neutralize and shield against EMFs.[14] As a general rule of thumb, anything that needs waves to operate (in other words, anything wireless) emits some form of radiation. While it's impossible to completely avoid this radiation, you can implement these steps to at least lower the amount of radiation absorbed by the body.

Another concern is endocrine disruptors. Many people are becoming aware of the harmful effects of endocrine disruptors on our reproductive health. These substances, such as pesticides, phthalates, plastics, and parabens,[15] can wreak havoc on our bodies by confusing and therefore disrupting our reproductive hormones,[16] leading to a host of health problems including fertility issues.

So many of these endocrine disruptors are present in our daily lives, from the food we eat to the products we use. They can be found in everyday items such as plastic containers, cosmetics, cleaning products, fragrances, and even drinking water.[17] The long-term effects of exposure to these chemicals can be devastating, affecting both men's and women's reproductive health.[18]

It is crucial to become aware of the harmful effects that endocrine disruptors have on our bodies. Because so many products contain these endocrine disruptors, we need to make a conscious effort to choose products that are free from these harmful chemicals and opt for alternatives. While it isn't always possible to completely avoid endocrine disruptors, we can become informed and avoid these chemicals as much as possible. Two helpful resources are https://www.ewg.org/ and https://www.clearya.com, where you can easily find products with clean ingredients.

The Light Leads Our Rhythm

Light is one of the ways that our bodies entrain with the environment. In contrast with the negative impacts of artificial light, sunlight has been known to have a significant positive impact on our daily rhythms, particularly our circadian rhythm. Our bodies are designed to function in sync with the natural daylight cycle, and exposure to sunlight plays a crucial role in regulating our sleep-wake cycle, hormonal balance, and overall health.

However, recent research has also shown that sunlight can have a direct impact on our reproductive health, particularly in women—studies have found that exposure to sunlight can increase the amount of cellular melatonin we produce,[19] and melatonin in turn acts as an antioxidant to cellular mitochondria.[20] As you already know, mitochondria are essential for healthy egg development and function, so this is an important benefit.

Sunlight exposure has been linked to improved hormonal balance, particularly in women.[21] Our bodies produce melatonin in response to darkness, which is crucial for regulating sleep and reproduction.[22] On the other hand, exposure to natural sunlight during the day can help regulate our melatonin production and promote healthy hormonal balance.[23] Note that melatonin impacts the cells in addition to being a sleep hormone at night.[24]

While sunlight is essential for our overall health and well-being, it's important to balance our exposure and protect ourselves from harmful UV radiation from the sun's rays. You can do this by getting your sunlight early in the morning (between 7 a.m. and 9 a.m.), when the UV radiation is lowest. Overexposure to sunlight, on the other hand, can increase the risk of skin cancer and premature aging, so it's crucial to wear sunscreen and to limit exposure during peak hours (11 a.m. to 3 p.m.). I often recommend anywhere from five to twenty minutes per day in the early hours of the morning.

Early morning sunlight can also benefit fertility by improving our bodies' natural vitamin D production. Vitamin D is vital for reproductive and pregnancy health. A deficiency in vitamin D levels has been associated with irregular menstruation,[25] PCOS,[26] infertility,[27] and miscarriage risk.[28] For these reasons alone, it is vital to make sure that you check your vitamin D levels when trying to conceive and, if weather permits, get daily morning exposure of direct sunlight.

It is also important to note that there appears to be a link between circadian rhythm dysfunction and irregular periods.[29] I like to compare our solar clock's relationship to our lunar clock to the minute hand's relationship to the hour hand—if the minute hand is off rhythm, this will impact all hands of the clock. The menstrual cycle is the foundation of reproductive health. If something is off with the menstrual cycle, it is essential to investigate the root of the problem by seeking out both conventional healthcare professionals and alternative healthcare professionals such as acupuncturists or naturopaths.

You can anchor your circadian rhythm by getting sun exposure as early as possible. This will let your brain know to synchronize to nature's clock. If you have a hard time waking up, you may have to push yourself to do this for the first few weeks until your body realigns its sleep rhythm. This may not work right away, and you may need to do it for at least a week before it has an impact on your circadian rhythm. If weather doesn't permit, you can purchase a light box, which is an alternative method of anchoring the circadian rhythm. You can find my lightbox recommendations here: https://www.michelleoravitz.com/the-way-of-fertility-recommendations.

While sunlight is just one aspect of alignment and balance, it is an important tool in the toolbox for improving your reproductive health.

The Moon and the Menstrual Cycle

According to traditional Chinese medicine and other ancient teachings, the moon's changes also play an important role in a woman's cycle. While the sun's 24-hour cycle is referred to as a "circadian rhythm," the moon's 29.5-day lunar cycle is referred to as an "infradian rhythm." The moon cycle and menstrual cycle have been linked for centuries, with many cultures believing that women's bodies sync with the rhythms of the moon. In fact, the term "menstruation" is derived from the word "moon" and is a testament to this belief.[30]

There are two types of moon cycles that are associated with the menstrual cycle: the cycle of the white moon and the cycle of the red moon. These terms are used to describe how women's cycles line up with the cycle of the moon. When a woman synchronizes her menstrual cycle with the cycle of the white moon, she sheds and renews her uterine lining with the new moon and ovulates with the full moon. When a woman synchronizes her menstrual cycle with the cycle of the red moon, on the other hand, that means she gets her periods with the full moon and ovulates with the new moon.

The moon cycle association is rooted in the idea that the moon's gravitational pull affects the tides and the water content in our bodies. Since the menstrual cycle involves the shedding of the uterine lining, it is thought to be influenced by the moon's gravitational pull during red moon cycles. Similarly, the increase of cervical fluid can also be seen as the rising of the tides in the white moon cycles.

It's important to note that, just as not all women's menstrual cycles are regular, not all menstrual cycles sync up with the moon. This isn't abnormal and shouldn't be a cause of concern.

Even though there is no official scientific data about menstrual cycles syncing with the moon, I have seen my patients' cycles sync up with the moon and with each other, and many of my patients have reported experiencing changes in their menstrual cycles during different phases of the moon. I often recommend they spend time outside at night to view the moonlight. I believe we used to be entrained to the moon's light before we became exposed to artificial light and that artificial light may confuse our internal rhythm when it comes to our infradian rhythm, as it does our circadian rhythm.

The Seasons of the Menstrual Cycle

The menstrual cycle is a complex and intricate process that involves various stages and changes throughout the month. Just like the changing seasons in nature, the menstrual cycle has its own seasons—the menses, follicular phase, ovulation, and luteal phase. These different phases can be compared to the seasons of winter, spring, summer, and fall, respectively. These seasons are not only reflected in the body, but they can be used energetically in a woman's life and in the activities she chooses during each phase of her cycle.

The start of a menstrual phase, the period, is the first season in the menstrual cycle. It's important to note that the menstrual cycle begins on the first day of a full bleed—spotting doesn't count! During this time, the uterus sheds its lining and a woman experiences bleeding for a few days. This season can be compared to the winter season in nature. Estrogen and proges-terone are at their lowest during the menses, and this can bring about the longing to hibernate and go within. In ancient times, this phase was believed to evoke supernatural powers in women.

There is a sense of opening the veil to our womb as it sheds its lining. This phase can also be seen as an energetic opening that may make women more intuitive. This phase is a good time to take it easy. I often recommend that women avoid exercising during this time and honor their bodies' needs for rest. Most women naturally feel inclined to relax during this time anyway, which is by design!

The follicular phase is the next season in the menstrual cycle. It is a time when the body prepares for ovulation by producing follicles in the ovaries. This season can be compared to the spring season in nature, where there is a sense of preparation for new growth. This is when estrogen begins to rise and signals the uterine lining to grow, evocative of the sprouting of spring. This is a phase when women may feel inclined to start new projects and be open to new ideas. During this time, energy starts to rise to prepare for the highlight of the menstrual cycle, ovulation.

Ovulation is the third season in the menstrual cycle. It is the time when the egg is released from the ovary and travels down the fallopian tube. This season can be compared to the summer season in nature, where everything is in full bloom and thriving. This is the time when women feel their best. They have the most confidence and feel most attractive right before ovulation, when their fertile window opens.[31] Women also start feeling more creative around this time.[32] This is an interesting correlation since creativity can be seen as mental fertility, while fertility can be seen as physical creativity.

The luteal phase is the final season in the menstrual cycle. It is the time when the body prepares for pregnancy by thickening the uterine lining. This season can be compared to the transition from the end of summer into the fall season in nature. Just as fall in nature is one of transition, in this cycle phase, the lining may prepare to shed if there is not implantation of a fertilized egg. Since ovulation is a short event, the continuation of summer expands into the luteal phase, while a drop in progesterone toward the end of the phase causes the lining to prepare to shed. This is a good time to begin slowing down and completing unfinished projects.

Understanding the different seasons of the menstrual cycle sheds light on a woman's rhythms and how they have a similar blueprint to nature's seasons. When trying to conceive, it can be beneficial for you to track your cycle, identify any irregularities, and take appropriate steps to support your reproductive health. Comparing the menstrual cycle to the seasons in nature also helps to normalize and celebrate the natural changes that occur in your body.

Grounding Supports Your Body's Life Force Vitality

Grounding, also known as "earthing," is the practice of connecting with the earth's natural energy through direct contact with the earth's surface. This practice has been used for centuries by different cultures around the world to promote healing and improve overall well-being. Grounding is an important part of our bodies' natural healing processes, and it is essential for maintaining optimal health.

Research has shown that grounding has numerous benefits for the body, including lowering inflammation and calming the nervous system.[33] Inflammation is a natural bodily response to injury or infection, but when it becomes chronic, it can lead to a host of health problems, including autoimmune diseases, compromised gut health, and reproductive challenges. Grounding reduces inflammation by neutralizing free radicals and reducing oxidative stress. It has also been shown to promote wound healing and modulate the body's natural immunity.

Grounding is thought to work by connecting the body to the earth's free electrons, which eventually creates an antioxidant effect on the body. Another amazing benefit to grounding, similar to the benefit of early morning sun exposure, is that it helps regulate the circadian rhythm. I often suggest that my patients ground while they get their early morning sun. I also suggest that they add breathwork to make it a power trio!

By reducing inflammation and inducing a sense of calm, grounding can positively impact fertility health. Many women who have PCOS (a common condition that causes reproductive challenges) have elevated levels of inflammation. Chronic inflammation also impacts gut health, which is a key factor in absorption of nutrients necessary to support reproductive health and pregnancy. Egg health and quality are also impacted by chronic inflammation as well as endometriosis, which is another common inflammatory condition that leads to fertility challenges. Grounding helps to regulate the body's hormonal balance by reducing stress and promoting relaxation. This, in turn, can help to improve the quality of eggs and sperm, leading to a higher chance of successful conception.

Grounding is not just a simple yet powerful practice that can have a significant impact on our health; it also naturally feels good and uplifting to place your bare feet on the earth. It is easy to incorporate grounding into your daily routine by spending time outdoors, walking barefoot on grass or sand, or even lying on the ground. However, if the weather doesn't permit, you can also order a grounding mat, which has the same impact and is used indoors. For a grounding mat recommendation, visit https://www.michelleoravitz.com/the-way-of-fertility-recommendations. Grounding is often overlooked as a natural and effective way to promote healing and maintain optimal health.

Incorporating a Daily Practice of Synchronizing with Nature

The information shared in this chapter is simply good information—until it becomes a practice, and then it leads to transformation! The following is what I suggest that my patients do daily.

Go out and get early morning sunlight. Spend as much time outside as you can, feeling the natural elements with all your senses. Become aware of the scents, such as those as of the trees, earth, or flowers; feel the breeze brushing your skin and the warmth of the sun. Listen to the sounds of the birds chirping, the leaves rustling, or water flowing nearby (studies show that the sounds of birds[34] and water[35] can reduce stress!). All of these sensations coming from nature have a naturally calming and regulating effect on our nervous system. If getting sufficient sunlight is difficult due to the season or climate, consider purchasing a light box, as mentioned earlier, in order to anchor your circadian rhythm to the light in the morning.

While you are out in the morning, ground your feet to the earth. If that's not possible due to your location or climate, consider purchasing a grounding mat.

Breathe using the full capacity of your lungs, slow and deep. Using your lungs' full capacity will awaken your body's vitality. Do this for at least a few minutes, as long as feels comfortable for you.

Having moments to connect with the elements around you in nature can help synchronize your internal rhythm. I also suggest eating foods that are grown locally and in season, as they too have benefits to keep you in sync with nature's rhythms.

A Return to Mother Earth

There's no doubt that nature is linked to conception. Fun fact: according to a study published in *Human Reproduction*, certain seasons have a higher level of conception and fertility![36] In North America, there seems to be a peak in conception occurrence during later fall into early winter. The reason why is not clear, but it may be of interest that this comes after most people have had a whole summer of sun exposure and vitamin D—or perhaps it's all the beta-carotene at Thanksgiving dinners!

As you can see, nature has an incredible power to heal and bring our bodies back into balance.[37] It is an ever-giving source made available to us. By getting morning sunlight, grounding, breathing in fresh air, and understanding the rhythms of nature, we can tap into this healing power and improve our overall health and well-being so that ultimately, our fertility health can thrive!

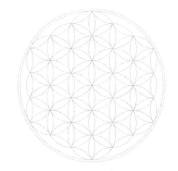

CHAPTER 6

Activating Our Reproductive Qi

Reproduction Needs So Much Energy to Happen

I f I could choose to focus on just one aspect of fertility as a practitioner, it would be energy. The amount of energy that is required for conception to happen can be observed in a woman's largest cells, her egg cells. The amount of mitochondria in an egg cell is dramatically higher than that in any other cell in the body.

Mitochondria, often called the "powerhouse" of the cell, are essential organelles found in eukaryotic cells, and they play a crucial role in energy production. As we discussed earlier, the number of mitochondria in woman's egg cells is significantly higher than that in regular cells. The reason behind this disparity lies in the energy requirements for reproduction. Reproduction is a complex process that demands a substantial amount of energy to ensure the development and growth of a new individual.

The high number of mitochondria in a woman's egg cells ensures an abundant supply of energy to support the early stages of embryonic development. These organelles generate adenosine triphosphate (ATP), the molecule responsible for powering various cellular processes. The increased quantity as well as the quality of the mitochondria in an egg cell provides a greater capacity for ATP production, ensuring that the developing embryo has ample energy for its growth and development.

When I work with couples on reproductive health, most of what I do for gut health, mindset, energy movement with acupuncture, and balancing the overall pattern all comes down to supporting their overall energy. Energy (as is encompassed in qi) is the Holy Grail of reproductive health and is responsible for creating an optimized state of vitality. This optimized state of health is the foundation to supporting new life.

There are many ways to improve your reproductive energy, but a big component of that is sealing energy leaks. This is where awareness comes in handy again, as you make note of what in your life makes you feel depleted. Things that deplete us can take a range of different forms, such as difficult relationships, unaligned jobs, processed foods, and over- or under-exercising.

Where Is Your Energy Going?

According to the law of conservation of energy, energy cannot be created or destroyed; it can only be transferred or transformed from one form to another. This concept also applies to our personal energy. How we choose to use and replenish our energy can greatly impact our overall well-being. If you feel depleted by the end of the day, it's important to note where your energy is going each day.

There are various factors that can deplete our personal energy reserves. Stress is a very energy-depleting state, as it taxes both our physical and mental energy. Overworking, lack of sleep, and unhealthy lifestyle choices also contribute to energy depletion. Negative emotions such as anger, resentment, and fear can drain us of our vital energy as well.

On the other hand, there are activities and practices that can nourish and replenish our energy reserves. Bringing awareness to what gives you energy is also very important. This could include eating certain foods or spending time engaging in activities you love or with people you feel aligned with. Additionally, mindfulness and self-care techniques like meditation and yoga are powerful ways you can restore and preserve your energy.

As mentioned earlier in this book, where you place your awareness is where you navigate and target your energy. This also has a way of magnetizing that which you are feeding energy with your awareness. Have you ever gotten really into a subject or activity, only to realize that, during that time, you began seeing things around you related to that topic? For example, when I used to paint and sell my art, I noticed that when I put my energy into the business and created more at home, I would suddenly get random interest from people wanting to buy my art.

This can also happen for things we put our attention on that we don't necessarily want to see. My patients often tell me that as soon as they realized they were experiencing challenges conceiving, they began noticing pregnant women everywhere. Although they didn't want to have a negative association around this, it constantly reminded them of what they were seeking but weren't able to have.

Plugging Your Energy Leaks

To begin plugging your energy leaks, start by journaling at the end of each day about what brought you energy and what depleted your energy. When you start this habit of journaling, you will naturally begin to increase your awareness of your energy throughout the day. Here are a few journal prompts that can get you started:

- How do you feel after seeing the people you spend most of your time with? (This can include your spouse, family members, coworkers, or friends.)
- How do you feel after a day at work? If you are tired, does it feel like you've applied productive effort, or are you simply drained? There's a notable difference when you feel like your energy is used productively vs. being drained.
- Do you feel frustrated or like your energy isn't going anywhere when it comes to your fertility journey? If so, what frustrates you the most?
- What is your least favorite errand or chore that takes your energy?
- Do you feel depleted from thinking certain thoughts? What thoughts are those?
- Do you find yourself spending a lot of energy feeling resentment toward people in your past or present?

These are just examples of getting really clear and homing in on where your energy is going. When you establish an understanding and get a clear picture, you are taking an important step toward plugging many of your energy leaks. As with all things, don't expect perfection. Instead, seek improvement in your energy. Perfection is another energy sucker, so apply all of these suggestions with ease and flow and address them with baby steps.

When you become aware of these energy leaks, this also shines a light on your inner workings and if they are limiting or benefiting your efforts. With your awareness, aka your superpower, you will be able to empower your energy efficiency and therefore learn how to contain important reserves so that they can support conception.

Harnessing Nature's Elements to Optimize Our Energy— Breathwork, Sun, and Movement

In chapter 5, I shared how we are an extension of nature and how nature is our guide. There are specific things you can do to improve your mitochondrial health and overall vitality. I shared how the sunlight can impact your circadian rhythm as well as your cellular mitochondria. I also shared the importance of grounding to regulate your electromagnetic frequency, improve your sleep, and lower inflammation. All of these are examples of how nature's elements can improve your energy and support reproductive health.

Another super important practice is pranayama, or controlled breathing exercises. Many of us don't optimize our breathing capabilities because we often learn how to breathe incorrectly. This can be due to wanting to hold in our abdomens or learning over time to over-tense our diaphragms from stress. Belly breath, which is a breath using the diaphragm, can be relearned through practice. Using the diaphragm not only allows for more oxygen intake, but it also relaxes the nervous system and can support digestive health.[1]

Increasing oxygen intake, which automatically occurs during activities such as exercise or pranayama, can help generate more energy in the body both directly and indirectly. Because increasing oxygen intake also regulates the nervous system, this allows for improved sleep and a better conservation of overall energy in the body. Yoga in particular has been shown to improve mitochondrial health[2] while also modulating the immune system in cases of autoimmune disorders and lowering systemic inflammation.

For years, traditional Chinese medicine has been teaching the importance of movement practices such as Qi Gong for moving and harmonizing the body's qi. These types of movements and exercises maintain the body's vitality and strength. While movement is necessary for overall energy and to support mitochondrial health, overexercising can have an adverse effect on overall vitality and reproductive health.[3] In fact, intense training can downregulate normal hormone production from the pituitary gland, causing a suppression in the menstrual cycle and/or of ovulatory function. This is yet another example of how nature reminds us of the importance of maintaining balance.

Using nature's timing in order to guide one's eating can also benefit our energy conversion. Ayurvedic medicine refers to our digestive fire as *"Agni"* and teaches that our environment can impact our internal elements. This is why it's important to eat the largest meal at the time of day when the sun is strongest, which is the afternoon, while having a lighter meal in the evening. This is the complete opposite of what many of us do in modern-day living. It is also important to have a few hours of fasting in the evening prior to sleeping. This will help your sleep to become more impactful so that your body can restore its overall energy.

Sleep

One of the most important and obvious ways to increase your energy is sleep! Sleep is not just a luxury; it is absolutely vital for our overall health and well-being. Sleep plays a crucial role in energy production and reproductive health. When we sleep, our bodies go through a complex process of restoration and repair, helping to regulate our metabolic system, nervous system, and reproductive system.

Sleep deprivation has been shown to disrupt hormone levels, particularly those that are involved in regulating the reproductive cycle. Insufficient sleep can lead to an imbalance in the production of luteinizing hormone.

Not only is it important to get proper sleep, but the window of sleep also matters. Research shows that overnight shift work in women can impact their reproductive health and ability to conceive.[4] Sleeping at night provides more restful sleep and allows for the circadian rhythm to be aligned with that of the sun's light. When this internal "clock" is off, it can impact a host of other cyclical imbalances, which can adversely impact the balance and regulation of our hormones.

In addition to assisting with hormone regulation, sleep also plays a vital role in the health of our mitochondria. When we are sleep-deprived, the function of our mitochondria can be compromised, leading to decreased energy levels and reduced overall vitality. This can have a direct impact on our reproductive health.

Sleep is essential for the restoration and repair of our bodies. During sleep, our bodies undergo a process of cellular repair and regeneration, helping to maintain the health and function of our organs and tissues. Without sufficient sleep, these restorative processes are disrupted, potentially leading to a decline in reproductive health.

Not only does sleep directly impact reproductive health, but it also indirectly affects other systems that are crucial for reproductive function. For example, sleep deprivation has been linked to metabolic disorders such as obesity and insulin resistance. These conditions can have detrimental effects on fertility and may contribute to hormonal imbalances that interfere with reproductive health.

Although it may feel like there is nothing that can be done to shift one's circadian rhythm, there are steps that can be taken to improve sleep. One of those steps is to consistently anchor the circadian rhythm by getting early morning sunlight, as we discussed in chapter 5.

Just like it's important to get early morning sun, it's also important to dim or minimize light in the evening a few hours before going to sleep. Light at night can suppress your natural melatonin production,[5] making it harder for you to fall asleep. If you must have screen time in the evening, then at least get blue light blocking glasses and/or set your devices to night mode in the evenings. Try to place any light sources low to the ground, as this lessens the chances that the body will interpret the light as daytime light. You can also encourage your body to relax by taking a bath, drinking herbal tea, or massaging your feet with lavender or chamomile essential oils.

It also helps to keep your bedroom cool and dark at night. If you have sources of light in your bedroom at night, you might want to try to use an eye mask. In addition, keeping a quiet space at night can make it much easier to fall asleep and stay asleep. You might want to sleep with earplugs or a white noise machine if you are also a light sleeper and find yourself often woken up by noises at night. For a white noise machine recommendation,

visit   https://www.michelleoravitz.com/the-way-of-fertility-reco
mmendations.

It is worth implementing these "sleep hygiene" strategies
because it is essential for both partners to get proper sleep to
support reproductive health!

Meditation Provides Cosmic Energy

Just like sleep is vital for restoring energy, meditation can
provide a different type of rest. Meditation not only creates a
state of internal harmony, but it also has an impact on the
quality of sleep you get at night.[6] Meditation also regulates
energy output so that your overall energy use becomes more
efficient.

As a meditator for over twenty-five years, I can attest to its
benefits, including improvement of overall energy. Meditation
feels like plugging your spiritual battery into a source of infinite
cosmic energy. It feels like taking a static radio station and
changing it to premium satellite radio, where everything is
smooth and consolidated. It is challenging to describe the experience, as it is something that needs to be felt personally in
order to be truly understood.

The catch is that when people first start meditating, they often
need to move through some rough turbulence before reaching
more refined energetic frequencies. This takes practice, and
what I find is that people may often mistake the rough turbulence for a sign that they just don't do well meditating and that
meditation must not be for them. My suggestion is to stay with
the discomfort because it is a part of a reorganizing of energy
that will ultimately restore and improve your overall vitality.

Meditation and Visualization of Inviting Cosmic Energy

Sit comfortably with your spine erect. Close your eyes and internally gaze toward the point between your eyebrows. Take a deep breath and imagine that breath pulling energy from the base of your spine, all the way up your spine, and into the back of your head.

Hold your breath for nine counts, and then slowly exhale, releasing the breath down the spine until you can't exhale any longer.

Hold your breath out for three counts and then repeat the process nine times. Nine is a power number in Vedic traditions.

Once you finish the breath sequence, begin to settle your mind into your body. Feel for any sensations or stagnation as you scan your body with your mind. Look to see if there are areas that feel more depleted or areas that are just stuck. Breathe into those areas for a few counts. You can stay as long as you feel you need to be aware of those areas. You can also imagine yourself releasing the stagnation down your spine into the center of the earth, where it will be recycled and used by the earth. As you imagine yourself cleaning fragments of stagnant energy in your body, begin to feel an emerging intelligent light source enter through the crown of your head. See it gracefully flowing into every cell and molecule of your head and traveling down into every part of your body. You may want to imagine the light clearing any stagnation you have remaining.

Feel the aliveness of this light, knowing that it has an ideal DNA sequence that is meant to protect and vitalize the energy of all your cells and strengthen the mitochondrial DNA. Feel the warmth of this light comforting you with a sense of security as it nourishes every part of your being. It feels like a comforting, peaceful, energetic bath, unlike anything you've felt before. Bask in this feeling for as long as you need.

Once you feel complete, you can imagine a membrane that contains this light surrounding you in your auric field.

This is a powerful meditation that can ideally be done at the beginning and end of each day. Over time, it will become easier to visualize the light in this meditation and go deeper into the experience.

Meridians, the Rivers of Life

In traditional Chinese medicine, the concept of meridians plays a crucial role in maintaining our overall health and vitality. Meridians are essentially the channels through which qi flows throughout our bodies. Just like how a river needs clear pathways to flow freely, our meridians need to be clear for qi to nourish and energize our bodies.

Meridians serve as the pathways that connect different organs and systems, ensuring a harmonious flow of energy.

It is essential to keep our meridians clear because the flow of qi through the meridians is essential for our overall well-being. By keeping our meridians clear and ensuring a strong and balanced flow of qi, we can enhance our vitality and promote good reproductive health.

In addition to acupuncture and acupressure, other aspects of a healthy lifestyle can contribute to keeping our meridians clear and promoting optimal vitality. These aspects include maintaining a balanced diet, engaging in regular physical activity, implementing daily self-massage, managing stress levels, and getting enough restful sleep.

The Simple Yet Powerful Practice of Self-Massage

Self-massage is one of the simplest ways to stimulate your meridians (yes, even if you don't know where the acupressure points are) because you're bound to massage many pressure points in the process! You'll also begin to develop a sense of where your body needs pressure most since self-massage improves your body awareness.

Ayurvedic medicine calls the practice of self-massage "*Abhyanga.*" In Ayurvedic tradition, this is done with warm oil. While you can certainly use warm oil, it is also beneficial to use room temperature bottled oil after a shower or bath. As an added bonus, you can also do dry brushing prior to showering to improve your body's overall circulation (more on that soon).

Another way to improve your overall vitality and qi flow is by massaging your ears. Your ears reflect your entire body, and yes, as acupuncturists, we learn the map of your ear and the areas that stimulate specific areas of your body. If you're interested in learning more, you can Google search "auriculotherapy points"; however, doing so is not necessary because, by massaging your whole ear daily, you will stimulate your whole body. If you do this along with a full body massage (as I will describe shortly) every day after showering, you will be practicing an incredibly powerful ritual that will regulate your nervous system, improve lymph and blood flow, and increase overall vitality in your whole body.

What you'll need:

1. A dry brush.
2. A cobalt glass container and carrier oil such as jojoba.
3. A few drops of your favorite essential oils.

Here's what you'll need to remember: all roads lead to the heart.

Before you turn on the shower, take the dry brush and start from the most distal parts of your body (your hands and feet) and move toward the heart. In other words, go from your feet to your groin (front and back) and from your hands toward your heart. Then massage from your buttocks upward as far as you can reach, from your abdomen toward your heart, and all other areas including your armpits, which have a lot of lymphatic nodes.

Once you are done, you can take a shower. After you dry off from your shower, take the oil and use the same concept of going from your hands and feet toward your heart for your massage strokes. Be very nurturing with yourself, and become in tune with how your muscles feel during your massage. Pay special attention to your abdomen, starting with a clockwise massage around your belly button and then massaging and stimulating your pelvic area.

Keep in mind that this should become very intuitive, as we innately know what to do to stimulate healing for ourselves. Our hands are our instruments.

Finish by cleaning your hands (so they no longer have oil remaining on them) and stimulating your ears. Alternatively, you can massage your ears with soap while you're taking your shower.

Another great habit is massaging your feet before you go to sleep. By doing this practice every day, you are implementing a very healing ritual that will improve your quality of life! Beware that it is very addictive.

Create an Energy-Producing Strategy

Ultimately, the strategies I shared in this chapter will help you to both seal and cultivate personal and physical energy in order to support your reproductive health. While these are just a few examples, there are many other ways you can improve your overall vitality, and your body has an amazing way of letting you know what those ways are based on how you feel! It really is as simple as getting to know yourself on a deeper level by tuning into the sensations of your body and allowing them to guide you.

Once you figure out what elevates you emotionally and physically, you can create an energy-boosting strategy! To do this, you will plan and implement ways to regularly engage in activities that support your energy and vitality. Chances are that this won't be a chore for you, as these activities will probably be activities that you enjoy, simply because things that give you energy are usually things that feel good! Some practices, like meditation, may start off more challenging at first, but eventually, even those practices will be things you can look forward to.

Creating a strategy to care for yourself in this way is the ultimate full circle of self-love. Knowing you are worthy and deserving of feeling your best will not only improve your overall well-being and reproductive health, but it will also fuel your battery and help you navigate the fertility journey with more support. The bottom line is that your energy matters and deserves to be nurtured!

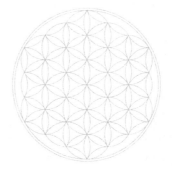

CHAPTER 7

The Heart–Uterus Connection

According to traditional Chinese medicine teachings, there is a vessel called the Bao Mai that connects the heart to the uterus. In traditional Chinese medicine, the heart plays an important part in the uterus's function and initiates the opening of the uterus. The uterus needs to be "opened" during ovulation to allow the egg in, during intercourse to allow the sperm in, during menstruation to allow the blood out, and during birth to allow the baby out.[1] If there is disharmony in the heart, either energetically or physically, this will impact the function of the uterus, which may reflect on the menstrual cycle and/or fertility health.

According to traditional Chinese medicine, the heart also houses the mind. This means that the state of the heart and the state of the mind are intertwined. If there is disharmony in the heart, it will impact the mind and cause mental disturbance, anxiety, or even, in rare cases, manic disorders. If there is a disturbance in the mind, which can occur as a result of chronic stress, fear, PTSD, or emotional imbalance, it will impact the state of the heart. This will subsequently impact the uterus and reproductive function.

So often, when women face fertility challenges, they are afraid to open up their hearts because of their repeated experiences of disappointment. But because the heart and uterus are connected, this can impede the heart's role in conception. This is something I frequently address when crafting treatment plans.

Many traditional Chinese medicine practitioners refer to the uterus as our second heart. What's really interesting is that the hormone oxytocin may play a key role in highlighting this connection. Oxytocin is responsible for our ability to form connections and establish a sense of belonging with others. This hormone is primarily produced in the hypothalamus and released by the pituitary gland. It is associated with various social behaviors, such as trust, empathy, and bonding.

Feelings of trust are what we experience when our heart qi is balanced, while feelings of distrust or anxiety arise from heart qi imbalance.

Oxytocin not only plays a role in preparing for labor (before the uterus opens to allow the baby out) but also during ovulation and orgasm. This earlier stage can also be considered a time for an opening of the uterus to allow new life to enter.

Oxytocin: The Love Hormone

In chapter 3, I briefly discussed the role of oxytocin as a love hormone. It gained that nickname due to its role in social bonding, trust, and empathy. Oxytocin plays a crucial role in many physiological processes, including labor and lactation. Research has shown that oxytocin levels increase around ovulation and after orgasm,[2] which suggests that it may also have an impact on conception and fertility.

When it comes to conception, oxytocin plays a critical role in the uterus. Oxytocin levels peak on the days leading up to ovulation,[3] which may suggest that oxytocin plays a role in preparing for ovulation. Oxytocin can also improve blood flow to the reproductive organs, which can improve the chances of conception by supporting healthy ovulation and creating a more hospitable environment for the sperm to reach and fertilize the egg. The release of oxytocin during orgasm may also impact fertility because it stimulates uterine contractions. These contractions can help to move sperm up toward the cervix, increasing the likelihood of fertilization. Additionally, oxytocin can stimulate the release of other hormones, such as luteinizing hormone, which is essential for ovulation.[4] Oxytocin may also play a role in male fertility.[5]

Oxytocin is also known for its impact on love and bonding. It plays a crucial role in social interactions and helps to create feelings of trust and empathy. This is particularly important in romantic relationships, where oxytocin can help to strengthen the bond between partners.

Something that has been found to increase oxytocin levels is nipple stimulation. In fact, some women use nipple stimulation as a natural way to induce labor, as it can trigger the release of oxytocin and stimulate uterine contractions. This same mechanism may also help to increase the chances of conception, as nipple stimulation can lead to an increase in oxytocin levels and improve blood flow to the reproductive organs.

The role of oxytocin in conception has not been actively researched, but it appears to explain scientifically what traditional Chinese medicine refers to as the heart–uterus connection!

The State of Your Heart

As previously mentioned, the heart houses the mind. One of the ways traditional Chinese medicine practitioners are trained to observe heart imbalances in our diagnoses is by noticing the state of a patient's mind. When people experience anxiety and emotional disturbances, it can be a reflection of a disharmony in the heart state. Similarly, a chronic state of anxiety and stress can also impact the state of the heart. Although there are other organ patterns that get influenced by emotional states, the state of the heart is an important focus that we treat to support reproductive health.

The energy of the heart can get impacted by many different factors that seem unrelated to fertility but may cause disruption in the heart–uterus connection. One factor that can cause this disharmony can be the relationship that a woman has with her mother. She may have grown up feeling unheard or criticized by her mother, or, if she saw her mother as someone who was very submissive, she may have felt a strong desire to become the polar opposite. A woman's relationship with her mother can influence her relationship with her own womb, and it may even cause a rejection of that part of herself on a subconscious level.

Another cause of disharmony can be sexual trauma or a previous violation that can cause a subconscious emotion of fear and tightening around one's reproductive organs, including the uterus. For those dealing with trauma or PTSD, I recommend first and foremost seeking a therapist and getting the appropriate support. Often, people hold emotions physically without realizing it. This can lead to years of pent-up disturbances that can impact the body energetically. I can't even count how many times my patients have experienced immense emotional releases during their acupuncture treatments. This is because acupuncture works powerfully to move qi in the body. When this occurs, old emotions have an opportunity to reemerge. While this can feel immensely uncomfortable, it is very necessary and productive to the healing process.

Harboring resentment and grievances is another very big factor for a disharmony in the heart's energetic field. This can be a tough one to resolve since resentment always feels like a justified response when we have experienced wrongdoing. The catch here is that resentment doesn't hurt the wrongdoer as much as it hurts the heart that holds on to it. Addressing old grievances should therefore be a priority in the fertility healing journey. It can be the single most powerful action one can take to address reproductive disharmony because harboring resentful energy can tax the heart qi and derail its energy from its important role in the uterus! When we liberate our emotional energy, we allow for it to support the sacred relationship of the heart and the uterus so that efforts for baby making are given an optimal chance.

Heart–Brain Coherence

Recent research is showing that the ancient wisdom describing the heart's relationship with the mind may be something that can be measured. The concept of heart–brain coherence, which refers to the energetic relationship between the heart and the brain, is also gaining momentum as an area of study. The heart and the brain are not just separate organs that function independently; they are also deeply connected to each other. This connection is formed through a complex network of neurons and chemicals that allow for the seamless exchange of information between the two organs.

Studies have shown that the heart and the brain have a synergistic relationship.[6] The heart contains an intricate network of neurons, often referred to as the "little brain," which communicates with the brain through the autonomic nervous system.[7] This communication system is bidirectional, meaning that the heart sends signals to the brain and the brain sends signals to the heart. The relationship between the heart and the brain is based on a concept known as "coherence," which refers to the synchronization of the heart and brain rhythms. When the heart and brain are in a state of coherence, they work together to create a more harmonious and balanced state of being. This can lead to improved emotional regulation, better decision-making abilities, and increased resilience to stress.

One of the key benefits of heart–brain coherence is its ability to reduce stress and anxiety. When our heart and brain are in sync, we feel more relaxed and centered, which can help us cope with challenges. Engaging in practices or situations that create a harmonious connection between the heart and brain ultimately supports a state of ease. This can be particularly necessary in situations with high stress levels, such as when we are faced with fertility challenges.

HeartMath is an organization that has been at the forefront of research into the connection between the heart and the brain.

They have developed tools and techniques that allow individuals to increase their coherence and improve their overall well-being. By using heart rate variability biofeedback, individuals can learn to regulate their heart rhythms and achieve a state of coherence. This can have a profound impact on their physical and emotional health and can help them to better manage the stresses of daily life.

The relationship between the heart and the brain is a complex and fascinating area of study. The concept of coherence highlights the importance of this connection, and research into this area is ongoing. Establishing a strong coherence between the heart and the brain strengthens both organs energetically. It appears that cultivating a state of calm and peace can support a state of heart–brain coherence.[8] From a traditional Chinese medicine perspective, supporting the mind and heart will simultaneously support the heart–uterus connection and, therefore, conception. Oftentimes this is missed when much attention is only focused on physical efforts of conception such as the best supplements to take or foods to eat. Even acupuncture is just one modality, but if there isn't enough effort taken to support the mind, all other efforts can be futile.

Since this aspect of well-being can be very abstract and hard to measure, it often gets overlooked. But addressing fertility health through an emotional well-being lens is vital and deserves priority.

Elevated Emotions

The state of our emotions impacts the heart. Scientific studies have shown that elevated emotions can have a direct impact on the heart's function.[9] When we experience happy emotions, such as joy, love, and contentment, our heart rate and blood pressure decrease, and our heart's rhythm becomes more coherent. This means that our heart is working more efficiently, which can have a positive impact on its role in relation to the uterus.

Cultivating positive emotions is essential for supporting heart health. There are many ways to improve our emotional state, and one of the most effective ways is through gratitude. Gratitude is the practice of acknowledging and expressing appreciation for the good things in our lives. Our emotional states are impacted by what we focus on, and this ultimately becomes our reality. By focusing on what we have rather than what we lack, we can shift our mindset to a more positive state. While there are many things that remain out of our control, what we focus on is something we can control.

Another way to improve our emotional state is to engage in activities that bring us joy. This could be anything from spending time with our favorite people to doing things we love. When we engage in activities that we enjoy, our brains release dopamine, a neurotransmitter that is associated with pleasure and reward. This can help to elevate our mood and promote feelings of well-being. If at first this seems hard, I often suggest doing things like painting, singing, or dancing that use a part of the brain that is more creative. This gets us out of our analytical brain, where we are more likely to focus on our problems.

Creating healthy boundaries is also important to protect our emotions. When we are engaged in relationships that cause repeated feelings of resentment, it makes it hard to elevate our emotions. When couples face fertility challenges, they often experience well-meaning friends and family giving unsolicited advice. While this advice is often coming from a good place, it doesn't always translate as helpful for those who are trying to navigate their challenging landscape. This is why it's essential to create an environment that supports us having elevated emotions, and during the fertility journey, this needs to be a priority.

Many of the boxes on the fertility journey checklist may focus on the physical aspects of boosting reproductive health, such as diet, supplements, and fertility treatments. We can now see why all those things may not matter if we don't address the importance of our emotional state. Just like planning diet, treatment plans, and doctor visits, supporting elevated emotions can be approached as a necessary strategy to nurture the heart–uterus connection!

Is Your Heart Really Open to Having Children?

You might say, "Of course it is!" and I'm sure you really do feel that way. However, we have this thing called the subconscious mind that holds onto annoying little hidden beliefs it's adopted throughout our lives. Allow me to provide an example!

Trinna was a patient of mine who put off motherhood so she could advance her career. She loved her work in advertising and held a very high position in her company. Many years before coming to me, Trinna had terminated a pregnancy that not only came at the wrong time but was also with the wrong partner. Trinna explained that she had looked at things from every angle and had to make a painful decision that there was no way she could move forward with her pregnancy. Years later, she had moved on with her life and didn't think much about her abortion, which she had made peace with. When she got married and ran into challenges trying to conceive, though, she began having thoughts that her body was punishing her for her previous abortion now that she really wanted to get pregnant.

Clearly, these types of thoughts were coming from unresolved emotions Trinna had regarding her history. Logically, she knew there was no way she could have made a different choice, but on an emotional level, it was hard for her to shake these thoughts. It can be so natural to have conflicting emotions, and it is vital to find a way to resolve them.

When I suggested to Trinna that she write a letter to the baby from her initial pregnancy and express her feelings about it, her eyes immediately welled up. Her immediate response to the idea showed me why it was important that she find some type of closure to the open wound she was carrying. She not only wrote the letter several times, but she also wrote herself a letter of forgiveness and self-love.

Although it was hard for Trinna to face her fears and pain head-on, it was precisely what she needed to move through the energetic block that had shown up in her heart. A few months after she wrote her initial letters, she decided to also write a letter inviting her future baby into her and her husband's life. That same month, Trinna fell pregnant!

While this story ended with a positive outcome, I want to state that each individual is very different, and that is why it's essential to get in touch with the thoughts and feelings you have about your specific circumstance. It's not the circumstances in our lives that create the blocks, but more our inner perceptions of them, all of which differ from person to person.

Thoughts can circulate around our minds without us even noticing. When we become aware of our hidden beliefs and question our thoughts, we begin to have a window into how to change the narrative of our subconscious minds. Our subconscious thoughts and emotions have a direct impact on our hearts and therefore need to be addressed in order to heal and move any blocks we might be carrying.

One of the most common causes for blocks that I see in my practice is unprocessed grief. Sometimes, such as after pregnancy loss, grief isn't given the space it deserves to be processed. Processing emotions that come with grief does not mean getting over or forgetting the loss. Many times, the loss of a pregnancy remains as a lifelong scar that will always reside in one's heart.

A Loss Is a Loss

Pregnancy loss is one of the most painful aspects of the fertility journey, and it rarely gets the attention it deserves. Many couples go through their experience of pregnancy loss in private, and therefore don't receive the comfort that is often so needed from community.

It's important to underscore that there is no right way to get through loss, and a loss of an unborn child is a significant loss. When experiencing a miscarriage, there are so many factors that come into play. There are the physiological factors that need to be addressed in addition to the emotional grief that is experienced after a miscarriage. There's also a need to understand why the miscarriage occurred so that changes can be made to avoid a repeated occurrence. Couples often describe experiencing PTSD for following pregnancies, which can trigger a state of anxiety at every doctor's visit.

While we can't take away the loss that occurred, it is important to have proper support, often from a psychotherapist who specializes in the fertility field along with pregnancy loss. It is also important to surround yourself with personal support such as family members and friends who are capable of creating a safe space where you can feel comfortable sharing your experience. It is critical to protect your heart in this process, and part of this requires feeling safe to express your emotions.

Like in the story of Trinna, if you feel ready and aligned to do so, you can write a letter to the spirit of the baby connected to the pregnancy loss, expressing your love for them and honoring their existence, even if it was brief. Holding a ceremony with a sacred ritual, such as releasing flowers into the ocean, may be a way to create a special gesture and acknowledge the importance of their life. This is a beautiful way to infuse meaning into their life while also honoring your connection to them. I have heard from many of my patients that they naturally felt called to doing this after their loss happened, and while it didn't take the pain away, it brought them a sense of comfort.

The Girl Who Appeared in My Dream

Shortly after I got married, I noticed I was a bit late getting my period. Now that my period was regulated, this was an unusual occurrence. I took a pregnancy test in the morning and didn't see anything, so I placed the test in the trash and went back to bed. My husband returned from an overnight shift and noticed that the pregnancy test had a faint line, so he took it out of the waste bin and realized that I must have missed the line since I had thrown the test out. He then came to wake me up to let me know.

An overwhelming flood of emotions came over me, and I began crying inconsolably. I don't know how to describe it, but deep within me, I knew it wasn't aligned for my pregnancy to happen at that time.

I cried hard, then fell back asleep. I had a dream of a young girl with long blond hair and blue eyes jumping on top of a washing machine, kicking her legs back and forth. I saw the cycle of the washing machine spinning underneath her. She spent a few minutes with me before leaving, and as she did, she said, "I'll see you later!" I woke up from the dream, went to the bathroom, and got my period.

I told both my husband and my mom about the dream. The strange thing was that, in my mind, the girl couldn't have been our daughter. Both my husband and I have brown hair, and I have brown eyes and my husband's eyes are hazel. It didn't make sense that we would have a blond, blue-eyed girl.

A few years after that moment, we had our first daughter, who had brown eyes and brown hair. As the years passed, the significance of the dream left my mind. Years after, though, my second daughter was born with blond hair and blue eyes. As she grew, something occurred to me as I looked at her long blond hair— she was the girl who had come to me in my dream. The whole story seemed so farfetched in my own mind that I had to ask my husband and mom if that dream was a figment of my imagination. Both of them confirmed that they remembered me describing a blond-haired, blue-eyed girl in my dream.

Years later, when I felt that my daughter was old enough to hear this story at the age of twelve, the moment I told her, she immediately cried and embraced me. I felt a visceral response immediately take over her, as if it was reawakening a memory that was felt deeply within her being. I feel like this experience happened not just for her and me, but for you and for the fertility community that I now serve. I had a moment where I connected to my spirit baby. The fact that it was my second was significant. If she had had brown hair and brown eyes, it may have seemed like a dream; the fact that it was something that would logically make sense to me made it a clear sign. Spirit babies are real.

Write a Letter to Your Spirit Baby (Exercise)

When I suggest this exercise to my patients, I feel their visceral responses. The exercise immediately awakens their heart centers and any pain that they are holding there. This authentic emotional response is exactly why this exercise is so important and why it's important to make this divine connection with their future child.

Similar to the above section where I suggested writing a letter to a previously conceived child, in this exercise, you'll write a letter to your spirit baby, your future child! Making that connection to your unconceived child can be one of the most powerful things you can do during your fertility journey. It taps you into the source of your heart's desire.

This is an opportunity to express everything you are feeling— your hopes and dreams but also your fears. There is nothing off the table here. You can also ask for guidance.

Here are some tips to prompt inspiration:

- Express how you feel and how you've been feeling. It is very normal to cry while doing this—don't hold back, as this is a very healing experience!
- Share with your future child how much you want them to come into your life.
- Share what you envision when imagining them in your life.
- Ask if they can show you signs or guide you to conceiving them.

If you have access to a beach or other large body of water, consider writing your letter on eco-friendly, water-soluble paper (if you need help finding this type of paper, visit https://www. michelleoravitz.com/the-way-of-fertility-recommendations). Once you have written your letter, place it in the water, imagining your message moving to a realm where your future baby exists as you watch the paper dissolve. Water is an incredible conductor of energy; it is also a yin, feminine substance. This is a beautiful ritual you can do to connect with your spirit baby!

Remember, you cannot do this wrong! This is a chance to fully express everything you feel regarding your fertility journey to your child!

The Power of Our Hearts

Traditional Chinese medicine has been teaching the importance of the heart's role in the mind and the uterus for thousands of years. Research has now given us evidence that there's more to this than originally acknowledged! I wanted to share an incredible research experiment demonstrating this that I learned about while attending a Dr. Joe Dispenza weeklong retreat in 2022.

At first, the baby chicks followed the robot's random movements. In the next phase of the experiment, the chicks were placed in a cage where they could watch the robot but were unable to follow it. That was when something miraculous began happening. The chicks' longing for the robot changed its random pattern of movement around the room to a pattern that moved closer to the chicks![10]

Dr. Dispenza said to us in the crowd, "If these tiny little hearts can do that, imagine what your hearts can do!" *Wow!*

We are just beginning to understand how powerful our hearts really are.

The Importance of Keeping Your Heart Positive

I want to also mention another important point about the other side of the heart and conception. So often, I hear stories from my patients about having difficulty with baby announcements and pregnancies. Over time, though, I've witnessed some patients move from resenting other people's pregnancies to eventually experiencing acceptance and even feeling shared joy in their response. This can be a very natural mix of emotions on the fertility journey.

While there are no right or wrong ways to navigate these difficult emotions, I want to bring up our human trait of mirroring. Neuroscience has discovered what they refer to as "mirror neurons." These mirror neurons respond to actions we observe in others.[11] For instance, when we watch movies and see someone act emotional, we may find ourselves tearing up, while when we see the main character triumph, we may feel a sense of pride. Similarly, when we feel positive emotions toward others, we subconsciously bring those back to ourselves. The same happens with negative emotions. Again, while there is no right or wrong way to feel, I simply want to bring up the idea that it can be possible to make the symbolism of pregnancy something that we reject subconsciously. The question is, could this contribute to a resistance one can develop toward the idea of pregnancy? It is important to approach this from a neutral perspective in order to not create a sense of blame or shame toward oneself. This serves to uncover emotions that are unacknowledged from a place of objectivity rather than judgment.

Although these questions may be hard to answer, they can serve as a light of awareness into the innermost state of our consciousness and may uncover hidden energetic blocks toward what we want more than anything. With or without these difficult questions, the blocks will remain unless we decide to acknowledge their existence.

Why We Need to Focus on Our Hearts to Conceive

Becoming aware of the state of our hearts can help not only the uterus and conception but also our well-being. The heart state is very responsive to our emotions. Making our emotional well-being a priority by choosing activities, relationships, and thoughts that support a harmonious heart is the single greatest thing you can do to support your journey! You deserve to feel peace and harmony at all times of your life, and the fertility journey is no exception.

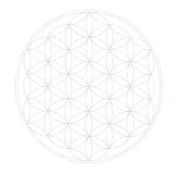

CHAPTER 8
The Magic of Flow

H ave you ever experienced a state of timeless presence where your life seemed to align with synchronicities and everything felt effortless? Most people have experienced at least one memorable moment in their lives in which they experienced this sense, which describes a state of flow. Many athletes, artists, writers, and musicians have spoken about moments of extreme presence where they were immersed in what they were doing. Coincidentally, their ability to hyper-focus allowed them to access a state of becoming superhuman, where they could touch an aligned potential in their profound presence. This state is not only able to evoke heightened talent, but it can generate healing potential as well.

The way I see it, flow is a state of intense alignment where the divine intelligence not only influences us, but merges with us to allow its design to be expressed in the way it was intended. This is not only the way of our highest potential as human beings but also our health potential as a whole. It's subtle yet powerful, a dance with the intelligent soup that we are made from. Some refer to this soup as the quantum field in which all that exists dwells, a remembering of who we are and where our power awaits us.

Flow resides in the present moment. When people get into an immense state of creative flow, their minds are immersed in presence as they become a channel for their soul's conception. If the flow state gives rise to a fertile and creative mind, it can also impact the body's fertility by exposing it to a state abundant with vitality. Flow teaches us that our state during the journey plays a key role in getting us to our desired destination: in your case, a baby.

Effortless Effort

Wu wei, a concept rooted in Taoist principles, is a state of effortless effort that is often a result of a perfect union of the yin and yang. It is a way of being in which we align ourselves with the natural progression of life, rather than trying to force or control things. In this state, we act in harmony with the universe, allowing things to unfold naturally and freely. Our actions are filled with ease as we become fully immersed in the present moment.

In the practice of wu wei, we learn to let go of our attachments to outcomes and surrender to the natural rhythms of life. Instead of trying to force things to happen, we learn to trust in the process. This doesn't mean that we become passive or indifferent; rather, it means that we approach life with a sense of ease and nonresistance. We become more attuned to our intuition and learn to act spontaneously, without overthinking or second-guessing ourselves.

When we are in a state of wu wei, we experience a deep sense of flow. Time seems to slow down, and we become fully absorbed in whatever we are doing. Our actions are infused with a sense of freedom, as if carried by an invisible force. We are completely present in the moment, fully engaged in our activities, and yet detached from the outcome. We experience a sense of joy and fulfillment as we navigate through life with grace and ease.

The flow that arises from wu wei teaches us that what aligns most with our well-being and harmony also *feels* good to us. The concept of wu wei reflects as a state of ease and peace. This is our most innate state, and it gifts us with a feeling of freedom as we are liberated from the constriction or resistance of a disharmonious state. We have been conditioned to resist flow and work overtime; going into this effortless state seems too easy and, at times, pointless. Because of this learned state of *doing* as opposed to *being*, the essential state of wu wei is often overshadowed and missed. Since wu wei is who we are at our core, rekindling this serene state can be more effectively approached by undoing our unaligned habits and patterns rather than seeking flow itself. In fact, the act of seeking will only lead us away from our *selves*, where this effortless state awaits us.

Flow Reflects Nature

Lao Tzu is said to have said, "Nature doesn't hurry, yet everything gets accomplished." Flow teaches us to honor nature's timing, having faith that all is in order as long as we don't get in the way. We have been conditioned to get things at a speed that is not compatible with nature's timeline. We expect instant results, and that invites disappointment. When we assert expectations on our lives, we are trying to control something that, in essence, is more of a dance between us and universal intelligence. By trying to impose our will on the outcome of our lives, we risk disrupting the flow of our lives and potentially generating unnecessary suffering in the process.

Trying to conceive is a dance that requires coordination of three parties: the two partners and the one child. Although as a traditional Chinese medicine practitioner I can help tip the needle to boost the probability of conception, there is still a mystery that is out of everyone's hands. I can never predict how long it will take a woman to get pregnant, or if she will get pregnant at all. Conception has its own pace and timing, and the more one tries to push it, the more constriction this adds to counteract their reproductive flow. Chronic stress has been shown to impact reproductive health;[1] ultimately, traditional Chinese medicine views chronic stress as stagnation of energy caused by chronic constriction or resistance.

A great practice for inviting flow is paying attention to how your body responds to things you resist or don't like in your life. Notice if you have any constriction in your body in response to your thoughts. Practicing this way of observing can help you recognize what is getting in the way of your natural flow.

Why Flow Matters to Fertility Health

Flow is a natural product of the yin and yang working together harmoniously. This is why, when we remove blocks through acupuncture points, the body is able to harmonize and create its favored state of homeostasis. People often have these blocks from years of unbalanced life habits or emotional states that work against the free flow of qi through constriction or resistance.

When the body is able to move its qi freely, all parts are nourished, and it is able to thrive. What traditional Chinese medicine teaches us is that the relationship between the body's flow directly impacts the mind's flow and vice versa. This is why stress can "stagnate" our bodies' energy and cause physical symptoms such as PMS, irregular periods, or upper shoulder tightness.

We can address our relationship with flow from either end of the spectrum. Working to create flow in the mind can impact the body, and creating flow in the body (through practices like yoga, acupuncture, or physical therapy) can impact the mind.

The state of flow is often a state of neutrality where we are able to bypass the natural push and pull of our minds. The push and pull of the mind is what happens when we either resist what we don't want or cling to what we do want. A state of neutrality is one of allowing the natural progression of our existence. This invites the flow of qi and allows for optimal healing and regulation to occur, both of which ultimately reflect in reproductive health.

Flow's Secret Ingredient

A bird begins uniting its skills to dance with the wind by using the power of its wings. At an appropriate point, it stops moving its wings and leans into the wind. It can only do this if it is in a state of trust, knowing that the wind will take over and keep it gliding in the air. This state of trust is what allows the bird to emerge into a dance and flow with the natural element of wind. If the bird, for any reason, stops trusting, this might disrupt its ability to fly.

Can you see where I'm going with this?

In order to allow the magic of flow into our lives, we must trust that we are part of a vast intelligence that is designed to work *with us* and *not against us*. Our faith in this intelligence is what empowers the magic of the placebo effect and other miracles to take place in our lives. Seeing patients coming to this flow by moving impeded energy through their meridians was a perfect way of seeing this flow in real time. Flow can be experienced as a state of being, and when we reside in this state, things tend to fall into place more easily. That includes our bodies' regulating process, as I often see with the optimized qi flow that comes from regular acupuncture treatments.

Sometimes simply trusting this vast intelligence seems too simple, and what I encourage is to just try it on for size. Even if you need to just pretend that you're giving over control to an intelligent force to regulate your reproductive health, try it; there's really nothing to lose. You can even try repeating this affirmation: "I trust that my reproductive health is improving every day, in every way." This is one small step in surrendering control and inviting the intelligent flow that breathes life into all aspects of nature. Sometimes the power is found in this surrender.

Anti-Flow

We are designed so intelligently that we will feel intensely uncomfortable when we begin veering away from our alignment or flow. I remember having symptoms when I was in an unhealthy relationship and when I worked in a job that I wasn't aligned with.

When I was in a relationship with a very critical boyfriend, I noticed I gained more weight than usual, had extreme breakouts on my skin, and lost my hair. The more that the boyfriend pointed those things out, the worse they became. After I ended that relationship, my symptoms improved.

In regard to my job, when I worked in architecture, my physical symptoms were warning signals of my being out of my natural flow. This was another example of my body screaming! I wasn't sleeping well, and I had immense upper shoulder pain, irregular periods, acne, and hair loss. What I was experiencing was the "anti-flow." The anti-flow seems like it's there to punish you, but if you use flow's secret ingredient, trust, you will realize that even the anti-flow is part of a greater intelligence and is designed to be uncomfortable so it can point you back into alignment.

When you come to realize that everything that comes your way is meant to be a signpost of redirection or confirmation, you will approach life with less resistance. With less resistance comes less suffering and more flow. All roads, even hard ones, have the potential to eventually lead to flow. Ultimately, we were designed to be in a state of flow. The more we come into this alignment, the easier it will be for our bodies to synchronize their reproductive health potentials in order for conception to happen.

Flow Cannot Be Forced

Trying to force flow is an obvious contradiction, yet many women who are told to "just relax" in order to conceive begin feeling an added pressure of having to force relaxation. This is an impossible challenge. When faced with discomfort or challenges, the only way out is through. Denying or resisting will only cause more discomfort, or anti-flow.

One of the most powerful ways to ease a person who is feeling pain is to allow them to feel validated and free to express their true self. This is something you can do for yourself as well. Remember, you are the most important person you need validation from. Allowing yourself to feel your feelings by talking them out to someone you trust is a way of releasing in order to come back to a state of flow. If you don't have someone you feel safe releasing emotions with, journaling to yourself is an effective approach (more on this in chapter 9, "The Power of Release").

When we understand that life is happening *for* us instead of *to* us, we realize that even obstacles are The Way. Everything that comes into our path, even if it's unpleasant, is here to teach us something. The flow we innately seek is really our natural way of being. Reclaiming this flow may sometimes be more about unbecoming what we are not and uncovering our natural state.

When I was misaligned in my life and even my career, this became more evident after I began having acupuncture treatments and felt like I was coming to life. It was as if I was awakening to the truth of my life and could no longer look away from what wasn't working. I look at alignment as a state or a portal of existence where all resources become accessible. Somehow, when there is alignment, things seem effortless and seamless. I believe this is by design, to let us know that we're on the right path. This portal of alignment invites healing on all levels and ultimately gets us to a state where we are rich with the vitality necessary to support new life.

Traditional Chinese medicine teaches us that, just as all of nature is like a hologram that reflects in all life forms, healing does not need to depend on one method. When I first began getting acupuncture treatments, they influenced the way I felt. Coincidentally, I was also reading self-healing books and starting a meditation practice, which influenced my overall healing as well. There are so many approaches to healing and ways to improve your fertility health, and the best thing you can do is spend time doing whatever brings you a state of flow and peace. This may sound too simple to be effective, but it's the small things that make the biggest impact. If you're not clear on what brings you flow and peace, think about what makes you feel most comforted or at ease, and spend more time doing those activities (or non-activities!). Finding flow even in small acts can have more of a transformational impact than abruptly changing everything with a "no pain, no gain" mentality.

Flow Asks Us to Listen

Divine intelligence is always speaking to us through our bodies (sensations) and our minds (feelings and insights). This is why meditation is such a powerful tool for aligning us with our greatest wisdom, the same wisdom that will always lead us back to a state of flow. Meditation has an ability to bring us to a state of receptivity as we quiet our minds. When this happens, we are able to access the connection we all have to our own innate intelligence, which can then create a coherence in our overall energy. This is why meditation has been shown to resolve so many mental and physical conditions. A meditation practice allows us deep relaxation, which can be described as a state of nonresistance, where we allow the body and mind to create order, coherence, and self-healing.

Flow feels good because it is good. When we begin to listen to what our bodies and emotions reflect to us, we can allow the divine intelligence to guide us back to the state we were meant to thrive in, the state of balance and flow.

It is important to keep in mind that listening has become a skill that we seldom practice in our modern culture. We are so distracted by information overload and the noise of our demanding lives that it is hard to go within ourselves. This is why the practice of listening—and I'm referring, here, to listening within ourselves—needs to be done proactively. It is a practice that requires daily space and time, and doing it regularly will produce immense benefits. It may even attract miracles.

The practice of listening to our bodies awakens our innate awareness. This can actually infuse an intelligent order that changes that which it observes. Our awareness may hold more power than we once believed. One resource on the power of awareness is the work of Dr. Joe Dispenza. Dr. Joe Dispenza teaches groundbreaking techniques for changing our physiology through our focused awareness. He has studied many participants who have attended his workshops, and they have discovered both physical and emotional benefits from the meditations he teaches. [2] He also noted a coherence that is seen in brainwaves where the waves work in a coordinated and cooperative way that represents a state of flow. Other studies, too, have shown that the practice of mindfulness can impact our physiology.[3] It appears, therefore, that our awareness has more purpose than simple observation; it also plays a role in creating a state of harmony, or flow.

How Coming Back to Flow Can Invite Miracles

In episode 61 of *The Wholesome Fertility Podcast*, I interviewed a woman named Lauren Hanna, a yogini and founder of Sacred Fertility Yoga. She has an incredible story, starting when she left a career in design when she felt a pull within her soul to work with people as a social worker and eventually leading to the founding of her fertility yoga studio.

In her early forties, she started her journey to try to get pregnant. Little did Lauren know that she would struggle for many years to become pregnant naturally. She eventually went to see a reproductive endocrinologist, and that's when she began feeling herself moving away from self-trust and putting all of her trust in the medical community. She tried several fertility treatments, all of which failed. She then began seeking healers and psychics, some of whom predicted that she would eventually have a baby girl.[4] After being told by many doctors that she was too old and that her egg quality was too low, she eventually went to India to see if she could get a donor egg. She had a transfer with a donor egg in India, but it failed.

When Lauren got home after her last failed transfer, she was so emotionally exhausted that she couldn't fight any longer. That was when she decided to move to a small cottage by the beach to clear her mind, body, and spirit with all the tools she had previously learned while taking a break from trying to conceive. She went back to her yoga practice, her meditations, and her mantras and cleaned up her diet so she could restore herself from the inside out. She did this because her soul thirsted for it. As Lauren came back to herself, she realized that she had given her power away to so many outside of herself—her doctors, the psychics, the healers, and other people in her life—when really, her own personal flow and power resided within her self.

Lauren found her flow and guidance by listening to her soul within. She feels deeply that the spirit of her baby gave her guidance when she stopped and listened. Through her meditations, the presence of her daughter came through stronger and stronger. The message she received was that she needed to become more present in her life. That was when she decided to fully surrender. This eventually led to her getting pregnant naturally at the age of forty-five.

When I interviewed Lauren, I had goosebumps as she spoke. Her story was so moving and real. Keep in mind that she was told by so many reputable medical providers that she couldn't get pregnant naturally or through medical treatments. Lauren was brave enough to go within and find her flow again, and in that flow, she found her alignment and her baby girl.

To hear more of her inspiring story, you can go to episode 61 of *The Wholesome Fertility Podcast*.[5]

Being in Flow Is Not Giving Up

There is a distinct difference between being in a state of flow and surrender and giving up. Just like in my example about how birds use their wings when they need to and surrender to the wind at the right time, flow is more about balance and alignment than complete surrender. Flow is knowing how to manage your energy efficiently, knowing when to be active and when to be passive so that ultimately, life moves more freely. Knowing how to optimize our personal energy by not wasting it on things that don't serve us helps us harness our energy for times when we need to draw from it most.

There are times when we cannot afford to sit back in the passenger seat, and there are also times when, no matter how hard we try, our energy gets us nowhere. When we feel ourselves hitting those walls, those are the times when it may be wisest to pause. While we have been conditioned that no pain equals no gain, pausing is not a weak choice to make. Pausing takes a lot of courage, and it also takes presence. Becoming present is actually an active choice to get into your innate power, the kind of power that resides within you. It's important to be mindful of why we are called to act. Is it coming from a place of thinking we should, or from a deep knowing within ourselves that we can only become aware of by listening to ourselves in times of stillness?

If this sounds too abstract, then I suggest becoming aware of your body sensations as you think about decisions you need to make. Does your body feel tense? Ask your body often what yes feels like, and then ask your body what no feels like. It takes time, but as you get to connect with your innate wisdom through your body, it will show you what feels right and what feels wrong. When something genuinely feels right, that is not a feeling of clinging but a feeling of liberation and freedom. We typically feel that way when we are in flow, because it feels open and expansive. Flow doesn't mean not doing work; when we are doing work that is in flow, our energy comes back to us.

Think of a time when your efforts were filled with passion, and, regardless of the hard work it took, it felt so good to complete the task or project. This is a perfect example of flow. It engages our effort with an underlying effortlessness, and it feels right.

Flow looks different in every individual because we are all unique and have different needs. That is why it is important to get into a habit of listening to yourself by becoming aware of your body's language and cues. Our bodies are so perfectly designed that they communicate with us all the time; all you need to do is start listening, and your ability to understand your body's language will increase because you will simply remember what you have been ignoring for many years.

Jeselyn's Miracle

Jeselyn reached out to me after struggling for over a year to get pregnant. Jeselyn's story is especially inspiring because she started with many autoimmune conditions that worked against her trying to conceive.

Jeselyn was on a mission to overcome the stress on her journey, and she actively worked with me to implement daily practices to ease her stress.

About a month into our work together, Jeselyn sent me a text telling me that I was a miracle worker and that she was pregnant. I was beyond thrilled, but I didn't expect what would follow.

Jeselyn came in after her announcement, but, while in my waiting room, she received a call from a nurse about her lab work. The nurse told Jeselyn that her beta levels (pregnancy markers), which were supposed to multiply, were way too low. Jeselyn realized right there in my waiting room that she was going to miscarry.

I will never forget the heartbreaking look on Jeselyn's face as she asked me for water. Jeselyn said that she needed to sit because she felt as though she was going to faint. Her face got pale. It was heart-wrenching to watch her in that state.

Jeselyn took some time to regroup after her loss, but she and her husband decided a few months later, with the advice of her doctor, that they wanted to do in vitro fertilization (IVF).

We continued acupuncture treatments, and she began listening to my fertility hypnosis audios (https://www.michelleoravitz. com/Fertilitymindsetmembership) to help prepare for her egg retrieval. The time came when she was supposed to start her retrieval after her period. But her period never came—because Jeselyn was pregnant for a second time. Amazingly, after she conceived, she was also told by her rheumatologist that her rheumatoid arthritis had gone into remission.

This time, Jeselyn's pregnancy resulted in the birth of her first son. After her son was born, Jeselyn got her period a few times, and then she texted me a mind-blown emoji and a picture of a positive pregnancy test. Jeselyn was going to have two kids back to back!

I also want to mention that before she got pregnant with her first son, I invited Jeselyn, along with another patient, to get a reading on my podcast from Julie Ryan, an author, inventor, and medical intuitive who predicted that Jeselyn might have multiple kids back to back. Julie mentioned that the spirit children come in orbs, and coincidentally, Jeselyn had a few pictures with orbs that she told me about ahead of her call with Julie. You can hear their conversation on episode 117 of *The Wholesome Fertility Podcast*.

Jeselyn is now a mom of two boys (a year apart), and she couldn't be happier! Jeselyn's spirit was what always blew me away. With everything seemingly working against her, she kept moving forward and didn't let anything get in the way of her flow. This doesn't mean that Jeselyn hadn't experienced moments of major anxiety, but she just kept listening to the message of her heart and began noticing signs all around her. She found orbs in pictures and a cartoon of a child with a rainbow in a magazine with the exact name she had always wanted for her child (rainbow babies are babies born after a miscarriage). She kept listening to the signs that guided her path despite the challenges she faced. Jeselyn's story will forever inspire me. You can hear Jeselyn's full story on episode 223 of *The Wholesome Fertility Podcast*.

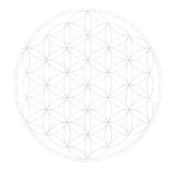

CHAPTER 9
The Power of Release

Held-In Emotions Can Cause a State of Dis-Ease

Both alternative and conventional medicine agree that the body's cleansing and detox pathways are vital for maintaining good health. We are not meant to hold on to what doesn't serve us emotionally or physically. When we hold on to anything that no longer has a purpose, it stagnates and uses up unnecessary energy. As mentioned before, reproduction requires an enormous amount of energy, so it is important to live a life that is as energy efficient as possible. One of the best ways to ensure this is to create a practice of periodical release.

It can be very easy to hold on to emotions without realizing it. This includes holding on to resentment or grief without providing those emotions a path of release. Our human nature tends to want to resist what feels uncomfortable. When difficult emotions arise, we may want to constrict or avoid them so that we don't have to feel the unpleasant experiences that they bring up. The word "emotion" comes from the Latin word *"emovere,"* which means "move out" or "remove."[1] Emotions are meant to move through us as we experience them. When we resist our emotions, we actually hold them in place so that the next time a trigger comes up, it reawakens them anew.

One of my favorite books, which expresses this beautifully, is *The Untethered Soul* by Michael Singer. In this book, Michael explains why we are better off leaning into these emotions and how, by doing so, we allow them to pass through us, which ultimately frees us from being bound to them.

Holding on to old emotions also keeps us from emotional freedom and living in the present moment. Holding on to emotions such as anger and resentment colors our lens of perception so that we cannot approach decision-making with objective clarity. It can cause us to act from a place of fear or distrust rather than a place of love and alignment. Increased cortisol, which can often be a result of difficult emotions or chronic states of stress, has been shown to impact the body adversely. We know that this can also impact our hormone balance, which is vital for reproductive health.

I have seen many of my acupuncture patients experience journeys of emotional release, and I have witnessed the benefits that that emotional release opened up to them when it comes to conceiving. I have come in after a treatment to see them drenched in tears, expressing to me that they haven't released emotions like that in a very long time. It's not just with acupuncture that I've seen this. Sometimes, just providing a safe space for my virtual fertility coaching clients has allowed them to feel comfortable enough to acknowledge and release old feelings they didn't realize they were holding on to. There are many ways to do this, and I will share in this chapter how you can also allow yourself to experience the healing benefits of release.

Digesting Emotions

Just for a moment, imagine your emotions as products of your life's experiences that need to be digested and released, just as your body does with your food. Have you ever noticed that when you experience a really emotionally heavy day, the only thing that can bring you the clarity you need to move forward is a good night's sleep? This is because, when we sleep, our brains process and consolidate the emotions we experienced during the day. This helps create order in our minds and can lead to a sense of balance and harmony.

We need to digest our emotions in order to free ourselves and our bodies from their excess energy. Again, reproductive health requires a ton of energy, which means it's vital to release anything that is depleting the body's overall energy. At first, digesting our emotions can take energy (just as digesting food does!), but in the end, digesting and releasing old emotions frees the mind and body from the heaviness of carrying them.

Digesting emotions is another way of processing them. Ways to digest emotions include journaling and talking them out. Sometimes, you can digest emotions just by sitting quietly and literally just noticing your body's sensations as you feel the emotions without judgment or getting into the story of the memories or thoughts that perpetuated the emotions in the first place. Pema Chödrön, an American Buddhist and ordained nun who has written several books, has referred to the power of learning to stay. This ultimately refers to sitting with whatever comes up and allowing it to be without judgment.

Witnessing your emotions or triggers can seem at first as if it will be very difficult, but it can be the single most empowering practice you can embark on. When it comes to fertility challenges, nothing can be more primal and triggering. From others' insensitive comments and opinions to your own opinions on yourself, every day can feel like a battlefield. This is why, when we enter a state of objectivity, it creates a space of witnessing without judgment what is happening within on all levels. Doing so allows the energetic entanglement of these difficult emotions and triggers to work themselves out and create order from what feels chaotic and binding.

When you begin looking at your emotions as frequencies that need to get processed and digested, it starts to feel like you have more power in allowing them to resolve. The antithesis is trying to solve them yourself from a state of emotional burden, which keeps you in a loop. Knowing that your emotions can resolve on their own with your presence puts you in a place where you can remain still and also allow your innate intelligence to do its job and clear you, just as it clears your digestion.

"It's Not Me, It's Just Something I Carry."

This statement came to me a few years ago when I was meditating deeply and also trying to resolve very deep emotions that were triggered by a challenging circumstance. Somehow, I came to the realization that I was not the emotions and fears I was experiencing. This also brought to light that, since I was not those emotions, I had a choice about whether I wanted to continue carrying them.

When I understood my role in carrying my emotions, it felt like such an obvious realization, yet it hadn't felt so obvious many times in my past when I was swept away by the anticipation created by my fears. I really believed that what I feared was real and that there was no separation between myself and what I felt. The truth is that the emotions I was experiencing were very old and had likely emerged during my childhood, and what had kept them alive was the faith I had in them and their repeated return. Repetitions, by nature, become ingrained habits. Our belief keeps things alive.

That is when I really understood the reality, which was that I could let those fears go. This was a liberating acknowledgment that also surprised me; I had never really seen it that way before. Being able to question the thoughts that lead to our underlying emotions is how we get to the root of those recurring emotions. This is yet another reason why meditation is so liberating— when we simply sit with *what is* and what we are experiencing, resisting nothing while allowing our consciousness to organize itself into the intelligent soup we are a part of, meditation shows us the truth.

Why You Need to Cry

One of the most powerful methods of release is crying. Did you know that the tears from crying are different from reflex tears (tears that come from a response such as irritation)? Tears from emotions release stress hormones, in contrast with reflex tears, which do not.[2] Crying itself increases feel-good hormones such as oxytocin and endorphins.

Crying serves as an emotional purging and is just as necessary as physical purging, yet it is often seen as something to be ashamed of. Almost always, when people cry on interviews on TV, you'll see them apologizing. Why is that?

We need to change our perception of this thing that makes us so human and connects us all! It's one of the first things we do when we enter this world, and it happens to be one of the best releases a person can experience. I often suggest that my patients watch a tearjerker if they need to release emotions so that they can purge their emotions through tears. Crying is a form of emotionally detoxifying.

It can take some time to get comfortable with crying, especially if it's something we have spent much of our lives trying to avoid. Some people may feel more comfortable crying alone, while others gain comfort from being around others. If you do feel more comfortable crying around others, it is still important that the people around you are those who will support you and not be harsh or critical of your emotions. Feeling safe is vital for releasing our emotions.

If you are finding yourself tense or easily triggered, chances are that you need a good cry! Sometimes we mask vulnerable emotions with anger or irritation, or we compensate with a tough exterior. True strength is also soft and doesn't need to be harsh. True strength comes from owning your truth in whatever form it comes—sometimes, owning truth means you need to break down and shed layers that no longer serve you. It's all part of the process of coming into your authenticity.

The important thing to realize is that nothing is going to compromise who you are at your core, as your true self is indestructible. Surrendering to your emotions does not threaten your integrity. The opposite is true, in fact. As you shed any excess buildup, you are able to shine your true essence, and your body is able to find a deeper sense of healing because it is not exerting more energy than it needs to. Releasing emotional weight ultimately allows your body to have less to carry. This essentially means that more energy can be used by your reproductive system for conception.

Transforming Your Emotions through Writing

When you engage in the act of writing with pen and paper, much of your intent, unique inscripting, and emotion can translate. This is why sending written letters is so much more powerful than sending texts or emails. There is a piece of your energy that goes on that paper. It's like a holograph that imprints your soul's signature and essence onto the sheet.

Ultimately, writing is another form of expression and can be used to purge emotions. When you write about something difficult, you will most likely feel the emotions as you write. I encourage you to write to acknowledge those difficult emotions as many times as you need to in order to feel a sense of release, enough times that you begin to feel less of a charge when you write. When that happens, you will know that the cord has been softened and you are not as entangled in the emotion as you were when you started. It's important to keep an intention of releasing and resolving these emotions while expressing your emotions through writing, and not in a way that reinforces a stronger identification with them.

I do want to point out that you don't always need to write about what's bothering you in order to feel released. Sometimes, you have an excessive number of decisions you need to make, and you may feel a sense of mental clutter or indecisiveness. This can happen if you're going through the IVF process or trying to make decisions about which path to take on your fertility journey. At those times, writing can be a powerful tool to help you get clarity when you feel overwhelmed. Writing out the different thoughts about your dilemma can also bring insight by clearing out any mental obstacles or concerns. There is no rule to doing this; in fact, it's best to just write whatever comes to mind so that you have a platform on which to place your thoughts.

The goal in any type of release is to emerge lighter, more energetic, and clearer than when you started. Any type of release is really about helping you get to your original essence, your core. This is where you find your internal balance fastest and get into your natural state of healing—the way you were designed before you accumulated excess energy and blocks throughout life. When I say this, I speak for all of us, as this is what happens when we live in the earth plane!

Journaling Exercise for Transforming Your Emotions

When you find yourself triggered by deep emotions, take the time to sit down and write about them. This ritual can be especially powerful when done alone, as it allows for complete vulnerability and privacy. Pour out your heart onto the paper, expressing everything you are feeling without judgment or reservation. Allow yourself to fully explore and delve into the depths of your emotions. The act of writing can be healing in itself, as it provides a way to externalize and process what you are going through.

Once you have finished writing and feel more liberated by the subject, it is time to burn the paper. Find a safe space, such as a fireplace or a contained firepit in an outdoor area, where you can light the paper on fire and watch as it transforms into ashes. As the flames consume the paper, imagine that they are also consuming your difficult emotions, freeing you from their hold. Feel the weight lifting off your shoulders as the smoke rises into the air, carrying away your pain and sorrow.

The act of burning the paper releases the pent-up feelings and provides a sense of release and catharsis. It allows us to transform those emotions from the paper, both literally and symbolically.

Remember to approach this process with mindfulness and intention. Set clear intentions before burning the paper, focusing on releasing what no longer serves you and finding peace within yourself. Take a moment to ground yourself before starting the burning ceremony, connecting with your breath and centering your energy. Allow yourself to fully surrender to the process, accepting and letting go of the emotions that have been weighing you down.

Using Our Voice to Release

Your voice is one of the most powerful tools you have! Your voice is a way for you to express your emotions through words, through singing, through screaming, and through laughing—just to name a few! The vibration your voice creates can shift the vibration of your whole body, as it can be felt throughout every part.

The part of our throat that represents our voice is a connection between our heart and our brain. It is a passageway that allows our deepest self-expression to be brought forth. If our voice is held back, figuratively or literally, our emotions can get stuck and create stagnation in our overall energy flow. Although it's hard to perceive the energetics of emotions because we cannot hold or touch them, they are real, and they impact our physiology.

Traditional Chinese medicine teaches that each organ has a role as well as an emotion. If our emotions have nowhere to clear, they get held in and stagnate the body's energy flow. When our energy is stagnated, it creates more difficulty releasing emotions. They often come out explosively, which causes us to experience guilt and shame, contributing to a difficult cycle that keeps us more stuck. This is one of the reasons why self-expression can be so difficult to implement, especially if a person has been having challenges with expressing themselves in the past. The transition and implementation of a new pattern of expression can be very difficult at first.

There are many reasons why people hold back from expressing themselves. One of the biggest is shame and fear of rejection. Many people who have this fear may remember times when their self-expression was met with criticism, which caused them to contract and hold back their voice. What it comes down to in the end is that fear is ultimately the most likely reason people hold back self-expression—fear of what will come out of themselves, fear of how they will be perceived, and fear that they'll be misunderstood or judged.

What can be deduced from this is that, in order to fully be able to express, one must feel safe. I can't count how many times my patients have felt afraid to express their feelings about their fertility challenges with friends and family. If they did express their feelings, they were sometimes met with insensitive remarks or unhelpful opinions that caused them to clam up even more. This is where boundaries can be very necessary. I often suggest that, if a patient has someone they feel safe speaking to, that would be an ideal source of expression. If not, they can find a therapist who specializes in cases of fertility challenges and loss.

Letting Go So That You Can Invite in Reproductive Vitality

When you begin a garden, you first need to take out the excess weeds. Imagine your excess emotions or blocks as weeds that are sucking out the nutrients and vitality that are meant for the new plantings in the garden. You wouldn't just start the garden without first working through the weeds, because you know that the garden will be much better off in soil that is first prepped and cleared. Now apply this to your journey to prepare for pregnancy. Your emotions and energetic patterns are real, even though they cannot be dissected and touched. They can act as weeds, subtly taking energy away from your mind, spirit, and body. This ultimately can take away energy from your pregnancy if it is not resolved.

When you are about to invite someone or something into your life, you first need to make room. By clearing out what doesn't serve you, you create an opening and space so that you can invite what you want into your life. One very powerful way for us to create energetic changes—besides the things mentioned earlier in this chapter—is through movement and ritual. When we act out a physical endeavor such as cleaning, it automatically clears our energy as well. Think of how much more productive you feel after cleaning your office. Purging things that have no purpose allows our minds to focus on what matters rather than get cluttered by the sight of things taking up space.

It can be beneficial to declutter your real-life space as well since our physical actions and rituals influence our emotional state of being. When we engage in activities of letting go of "things," this can have a therapeutic effect on our emotions. I highly recommend that, if you tend to accumulate a lot of clutter in your space, you create regular intervals of decluttering and giving away belongings that you know you don't use and don't need to keep. Doing this might be difficult at first, but you don't need to do it all at once. In fact, it might be good to give yourself ten minutes a day where you organize a small part of your space. If you naturally want to spend more time and can afford to, then have at it! Decluttering is not just a great concept; it has been shown to lower stress, while having clutter increases stress.[3]

Through release and nonattachment, we learn that we are whole as we are, without anything extra. It is our purest presence underneath all our excess layers that holds our greatest vitality and path to healing. This is because we are designed at our core to thrive and reproduce. When we allow our inner being to shine, we automatically invite health and balance into our lives, which reflects in our innate physical creativity, aka fertility.

Visualization on Releasing Deep Emotions

A very powerful way to release deep emotions is through a combination of visualization and breathwork. This is where awareness comes in handy. Paying attention to the subtle sensations in the body when you bring up past emotional triggers is a powerful way of awakening them so they can become accessible for release. So often, people want to resist triggers, but when they are activated, an opportunity to release them arises.

If you are open to it, the following exercise can be a good way to begin this process. To start, bring up a memory that you consider a trigger or emotional charge. I suggest doing this when no one else is home and you can feel free to release uninterrupted. If the memory is deeply traumatic, it is best to speak to a qualified therapist or counselor first, before bringing it up on your own. Otherwise, allow this memory and the feelings associated with it to surface. When you feel deep emotions being evoked and awakened, breathe deeply and then release that breath with a powerful exhale.

You can add a strong sigh or even a loud sound to release this emotion. There is a powerful effect in releasing through breath and sound; this is why people often feel the need to yell or cry loudly if they have a lot of deep emotion coming up. It's necessary to allow sound to help the release, and this is an innate response that we have before we even learn to speak. Most of the time, we learn to feel our emotions privately as well as quietly. This contributes to a lot of emotional stagnation, and the longer emotion stagnates, the more it builds. Give yourself permission to release it all. You may even want to say out loud a few times, "It is safe for me to release what I've been carrying for so long." This statement alone can evoke an emotional response.

After releasing this emotion through breath and sound, you can also shake your body strongly. Let go of any judgment; just allow yourself to be in the moment, moving your body the way it wants to move. Our bodies hold a lot of emotions, and shaking is a powerful way to release these emotions. Animals will often shake after a traumatic experience to release the buildup of energy. This is another example of nature's wise teachings. Shaking also moves us into a state of surrender, creating rapid movement that we cannot easily resist.

When you feel complete with this exercise, slowly take a deep breath in and out and lie down on your back for five to ten minutes so that your nervous system can reorganize and process the release. You can listen to music when doing this whole exercise, ending with calming and meditative music. You can also imagine a white, healing light enveloping and sealing your aura as you lie down.

Exercise Using Grounding to Release Our Emotions into the Ground

Another powerful exercise to help release our emotions is using the powerful healing energy of nature. Just like nature provides us food, water, circadian regulation, oxygen, and so much more, it also provides an endless and often untapped supply of gifts. One of nature's gifts is its extraordinary ability to assist our cleansing, both physically and emotionally. This exercise combines both connecting to the earth and visualization in order to release stagnant energy out of our bodies. While our bodies tend to hold this energy, the earth can transform it and reuse it. This becomes a symbiotic relationship we have to the earth that benefits the whole. We are gaining while, at the same time, providing.

Ideally, you can sit on grass or even sand on the beach so that your sacrum is touching the earth as you do this exercise. An alternative is to sit on a grounding mat (avoid doing so if there's lightning outside, though). Sit with your legs crossed and spine erect. Begin this practice by taking three deep inhalations and exhalations. Then begin imagining the area around your tailbone having invisible roots that move down deeply into the middle of the earth. With every inhalation, imagine sipping new vital energy from the earth like a straw. With each exhalation, imagine releasing blocks from your energy centers back into the middle of the earth, where they can be transformed and reused by nature. Continue imagining this with your breath. You can imagine it as purifying energy that binds to any stagnant energy and takes it back down into the earth.

As you continue this practice, you may begin to feel things come up that you weren't aware of before, such as stuck energy in different areas of your spine or in the front of your body. You may become more aware of the tension that you are holding in your muscles. If so, this is a great thing, as it provides more insight and awareness into what needs to get released. Keep breathing the energy from the earth into those areas and see it grab (like a magnet) any stagnation and pull it down into the earth with each exhalation. Continue until you feel complete.

At the end of this practice, visualize a bubble of light around you, sealing your aura. You can also visualize this bubble of light feeding all your organs and cells with healing vitality. The more you learn to make releasing a maintenance practice, the more you can chip away from any blocks that are getting in the way of your life force vitality. Ultimately, this life force is the source that will feed your reproductive health.

Practice Maintaining Your Emotional and Energetic Hygiene

Providing yourself with consistent practices of letting go is an important way to maintain your emotional hygiene. Just because you can't see your energy and emotions doesn't mean they aren't potent and aren't influencing your body and mind. We often carry a lot of excess emotional weight that we may not even realize we are carrying. This is why it's important to check in with yourself often. By doing so, you are adding an element to your self-care routine that ensures your release of that which no longer serves you so that you can become liberated and can thrive!

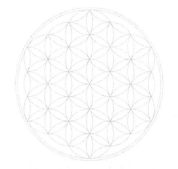

CHAPTER 10

Harmonize

After Release, Harmonize

Once we remove the obstacles that get in the way, the body goes into a state of wanting to create balance and harmony, as described in chapter 4. This may feel uncomfortable for a period of time, as balance coming after an imbalance can tilt back and forth at first. That is why it's important to approach harmonization with an action plan.

Harmony is beautifully depicted in the Serenity Prayer, which so eloquently states, "God grant me the serenity to accept the things I cannot change, the courage to change the things I can, and the wisdom to know the difference."[1] When we say the

Serenity Prayer, we are asking to be in a state where our energy can be used where it is able to be used and surrendered where it isn't helpful; we are asking for our energy to be used in a way that is efficient and in balance. Harmonizing includes creating a state within ourselves that is neutral—not pushing or pulling too hard. This state is one of being in our natural flow, a state of effortless effort or wu wei, as discussed in chapter 8. This is the ideal state for the body to self-heal.

If yin and yang had a baby, her name would be harmony. While the yin and yang are two opposites that depend on each other for balance, harmony is the by-product of this balance. To harmonize is to oscillate between two opposing energies in order to find a coherent balance. Both yin and yang need to be awake for this. Sometimes, you will need to experience a larger oscillation to strengthen both opposites so they can wind up harmonizing more effectively. All roads can lead to this harmony, but intention is the driver.

The opportunity for harmony is all around us. Our intention steers our focus to perceive our opportunity so that we can bring ourselves back home to our most authentic state of being. Harmony's by-product is the natural flow of life and vitality. It is bending and compromising while remaining steadfast in its desire to blossom. Harmony is sacredly immersed in The Way.

The essence of harmony is embedded in our blueprint. We naturally recognize harmony because we are hardwired to seek it; it is our own primordial mother, the one who brings us forth. When we understand our true nature, not only are we *able* to return to harmony, but we also discover that we *are* harmony. To truly harmonize means to be whole with every aspect of ourselves. This means allowing what we experience without judgment so that our harmonious nature can express itself unimpeded.

For women, this inner state of harmony is the underlying force behind our reproductive health and menstrual cycle. The endocrine system is like its own ecosystem, with rhythms, pulses, and signals that always seek harmony. Hormones get activated and paused throughout each day, signaling the body to keep them optimally balanced. An amazing symphony takes place to make the body fertile. Connecting to this harmonious state is at the core of fertility health.

We Are Vibration

We can access harmony through vibration. Vibrations play a crucial role in our daily lives; vibration is what inherently connects us to the world around us. We ourselves emit vibrations, and we are constantly responding to vibrations of all kinds, including the sound waves we hear, the energy that surrounds us, and the frequency at which our emotions resonate. By understanding the profound impact that these vibrations have on us, we can harness their harmonious potential to improve our overall well-being.

Vibration is not limited to sound waves alone; it extends to all forms of energy. Our bodies are composed of vibrating atoms and molecules that generate their own unique frequency. This frequency determines our overall state of being, including our physical, emotional, and mental well-being. When we are in a state of balance and harmony, our vibrations are aligned, and we radiate coherent energy. Conversely, when our vibrations are disrupted or out of sync, we may experience feelings of unease or discomfort.

People tend to be tuned in more closely to a specific vibration. This is why, at times, people feel that they are on the "same wavelength" as others. It's because those people tend to resonate or harmonize with a shared wavelength, which affects their thoughts, observations, perceptions, and behavior.

Kirlian photography is an amazingly tangible way of showing us that we emit different light frequencies. Kirlian photography, a type of electro-photography that can reveal an image of the energy field surrounding an object or person, was invented by a Russian electrician named Semyon Davidovich Kirlian in 1939. The energy field has been shown to change depending on the subject's stress level or environment.[2]

I have gotten my photograph taken with a Kirlian camera a number of times over several years, and while the photos displayed slight changes in my energy range, I was amazed at the fact that it stayed remarkably consistent. I have also seen my mom's and husband's photographs, which each looked completely unique and different. This has shown me that the Kirlian photography images picked up each unique vibration.

Each human holds their own unique vibration while constantly responding to vibrations of all kinds. By cultivating awareness of the vibrations we emit and receive, we can consciously choose to align ourselves with positive frequencies and invite more harmony into our bodies.

When we allow ourselves to loosen our grip on one specific vibration or "mental home," that opens us up to a vast array of tools that we can use to navigate this thing called life. We begin to attract new possibilities and allow ourselves to finally vibrate with the light of universal consciousness and intelligence. When we do, we can enter wholeness and healing. This in turn opens us up to a self-healing state, which will reflect in our reproductive health, as our innate essence naturally seeks to expand itself into new life. Remember, reproduction is ingrained in our blueprint.

Using Sound to Harmonize Our Energy

Sound has a remarkable power to harmonize our bodies and our energy. Studies suggest that the vibrations created by sound can have a profound impact on our well-being.[3] Since ancient times, people have used the power of sound to heal and restore balance within themselves. Chanting mantras and listening to soothing sounds can help us connect with our inner selves and can create a sense of peace and tranquility. The frequency of the sound waves we hear can directly affect our moods, emotions, and overall energy levels. Humming can also stimulate our vagus nerve, which is responsible for regulating a myriad of body functions such the digestive system and heart rate.

Chanting in particular is a powerful technique that has been used for centuries to bring about healing and transformation. When we chant a mantra, we are creating a specific vibration that resonates with our bodies and energy. This vibration helps to clear any blockages or imbalances within us, allowing energy to flow freely. The rhythmic repetition of the mantra creates a sense of calmness and focus, helping us to let go of stress and tension. Regular chanting can help us to maintain a state of balance and harmony in our lives.

The sounds around us in nature have the potential to impact how we feel. Have you ever noticed how the sound of birds chirping or waves crashing against the shore can instantly uplift your mood? This is because these natural sounds carry healing vibrations that can have a positive effect on our well-being. Research has shown that exposure to natural sounds can reduce stress, lower blood pressure, and improve sleep quality.[4] The vibrations from nature are truly healing and can help us align our bodies and energy with the natural rhythm of life.

Each energy center in the body responds to different sound frequencies. When optimizing fertility, it is essential that we realize we need to focus on all our energy centers, not just our reproductive center. Chanting and being surrounded by natural sounds found in nature are two great examples of how we can invite harmony into our energetic field. We can also do this by listening to specific sounds that have been shown to have a healing effect, such as classical music, Solfeggio frequencies, binaural beats, or sound bowls.

Sacred Geometry Vibration (Flower of Life Embryos)

Sacred geometry is a fascinating concept that has intrigued humans for centuries. It is the study of geometric shapes and patterns that are believed to hold spiritual significance. One of the most well-known symbols in sacred geometry is the flower of life, which consists of overlapping circles forming a beautiful pattern. This symbol can be found in various ancient cultures and civilizations and is often associated with creation and fertility. The flower of life is said to represent the divine blueprint of all creation, and it is believed to contain the secrets of the universe within its intricate design.

The connection between sacred geometry and the embryo is truly remarkable. When we observe the early stages of embryonic development, we can see the presence of geometric patterns that resemble those found in sacred geometry. This suggests that these patterns are not only prevalent in nature but also play a fundamental role in the process of creation itself. The embryo can be seen as a physical manifestation of sacred geometry, representing the potential for life and growth.

The Fibonacci sequence is another mathematical formula that holds significant symbolism in sacred geometry. This sequence, discovered by Leonardo Fibonacci, is a series of numbers in which each number is the sum of the two preceding ones (1, 1, 2, 3, 5, 8, 13 . . .). This sequence can be found in various aspects of nature, such as the arrangement of leaves on a stem or the spiral pattern of a seashell. The Fibonacci sequence is believed to represent the inherent harmony and balance in nature, reflecting the interconnectedness of all things.

The use of sacred geometry and its symbols extends beyond its aesthetic appeal. It is believed that these geometric patterns emit specific vibrations that can have a profound impact on our well-being and healing. By meditating or focusing on these symbols, we can align ourselves with their energetic frequencies, promoting balance and harmony within our own bodies and minds. This practice has been used for centuries in various ancient civilizations as a means of spiritual and physical healing.

The ancient origins of sacred geometry and its symbols only add to their allure and mystique. These concepts have been passed down through generations, woven into the fabric of ancient cultures and religions. You can access a powerful flower of life kaleidoscope meditation in my Fertility Mindset Hypnosis & Toolbox Library membership (https://www.michelleoravitz. com/Fertilitymindsetmembership). While meditating on the flower of life can be a powerful practice that evokes a vibration of fertility and growth, you can also simply take a walk in nature and look at the flowers and leaves to gaze on the natural expressions of nature's geometric sequence. Using your vision is another way to create harmony in every part of your being.

Our Chakra System

A beautiful example of the interplay of connected and interchanging vibrations is the human chakras. "Chakras" literally translates as "energy wheels," and chakras are located in seven specific centers of your body. Just as the earth has several vortices, the chakras can be considered the body's vortices. When they are healthy and vibrant, their energy spins like a wheel. Each chakra not only works within its own purpose, but they also interdepend and interact with their neighbors. A harmonious interaction between and within chakras will ultimately invite robust reproductive health, since all systems need to work in tandem to support new life.

Each chakra also has a color and a sound that it vibrates to. These are not just pretty symbols that happen to look like a rainbow when they are combined; the colors actually have vibrations, and the vibrations move from reflecting the lowest number of light fragments (red) to reflecting all light fragments (white). If you want to learn more about the specifics of each chakra, including their colors, energetics, mantras, and the crystals that harmonize them, go to www.michelleoravitz.com/thewayoffertilityresources.

Using Scent to Harmonize

Essential oils have long been known for their therapeutic properties and their ability to enhance our well-being. The olfactory nerve, which is responsible for our sense of smell, has a direct connection to the brain. This means that scents can have a direct impact on our state of mind. By using essential oils, we can harness the power of these scents to promote relaxation, reduce stress, and improve our overall mental and emotional health.

When it comes to fertility, essential oils can be a valuable tool. There are certain essential oils that have been shown to have positive effects on fertility and reproductive health. These oils can be used in a variety of ways; they can be added to a bath, diffused in the air, or combined with carrier oils and applied topically to the skin. In addition to their potential benefits for fertility, essential oils can also be used during meditation. Using essential oils during meditation creates an association between the scent and relaxation, allowing you to more quickly enter a state of calm and tranquility.

Some essential oils that are particularly beneficial for fertility include clary sage, lavender, ylang ylang, geranium, sandalwood, chamomile, and frankincense. Each of these oils has unique properties that can support reproductive health and balance hormones. Keep in mind that many essential oils are contraindicated during pregnancy, so once you become pregnant, it's best to pause their use or check with a medical professional.

- **Clary sage oil:** Clary sage oil is a remarkable tool for promoting fertility and overall menstrual health. It has numerous benefits for women's well-being, both physically and emotionally. This oil can help alleviate anxiety, stress, and depression while also providing relief from menstrual cramps. Additionally, clary sage oil aids in balancing hormones, promoting menstruation, and lowering blood pressure. It even stimulates the sacral and third-eye chakras, enhancing the mind–body connection. I recommend not using clary sage after ovulation in months you are actively trying to conceive; it's typically best for preparing the body before actively trying. It is particularly contraindicated for pregnancy.
- **Lavender oil:** Lavender oil has been found to have numerous benefits for women's reproductive health. One of the key benefits of lavender oil is its ability to promote menstrual balance. While there is no decisive evidence that lavender oil can induce menstruation, it has been shown to reduce menstrual pain and discomfort. This can be incredibly helpful for women who struggle with painful periods. Additionally,

lavender oil has the added bonus of promoting relaxation and regulating sleep, which can further support overall fertility health.

- **Ylang ylang oil:** Ylang ylang is a powerful essential oil that has numerous benefits, especially when it comes to fertility health. Its balancing properties can help regulate menstrual cycles, improve circulation, increase libido, and promote overall reproductive wellness. Ylang ylang's ability to soothe the stomach and calm sexual energies can also contribute to a healthier reproductive system.

- **Geranium oil:** Geranium oil has a wide range of benefits for fertility and menstrual health. It is believed to have antioxidant, antibacterial, anti-inflammatory, antimicrobial, and astringent properties. When it comes to fertility, geranium oil can play a role in balancing hormones and supporting the reproductive system. It can help regulate the menstrual cycle and alleviate symptoms of PMS. Additionally, geranium aromatherapy massage has been shown to improve physical and mental symptoms of PMS by increasing cerebral blood flow.

- **Sandalwood oil:** While there may not be extensive scientific research to support it, sandalwood is frequently used in Ayurvedic remedies and has long been regarded as an aphrodisiac and a fertility helper. Both men and women can benefit from using sandalwood essential oil, as it has been widely suggested for promoting fertility. Its balancing properties can help regulate menstrual cycles and hormonal imbalances, which are often key factors in fertility issues. Sandalwood is a great scent to use for meditation.

- **Chamomile oil:** Chamomile oil has numerous benefits that can benefit the menstrual cycle and fertility health. It can decrease symptoms of PMS and is calming for the nervous system. Chamomile can reduce stress and anxiety, aid digestion, and help insomnia. Diffusing chamomile can be beneficial for meditation or stress relief.
- **Frankincense oil:** Frankincense oil offers a range of benefits for fertility and menstrual health. It has been widely studied and has been found to help balance hormones, promote digestion, and boost libido, among other benefits. Frankincense oil can help regulate menstrual cycles, reduce mood swings, and alleviate symptoms associated with menstruation. Frankincense is also beneficial for moving stagnation and may benefit conditions such as endometriosis and fibroids.

However, it is important to be aware that essential oils are potent and should be used with caution. Before using any essential oil, it is always a good idea to do some research or consult with a healthcare professional to ensure that it is safe for you. I recommend using organic essential oils when possible and avoiding taking any of them internally. In addition, some essential oils may cause skin irritation or other adverse reactions, so it is important to dilute them properly before applying them to the skin.

Chakra-Harmonizing Meditation

The chakra-harmonizing meditation is a powerful practice that allows us to connect with our bodies' energy centers and bring balance to our physical, mental, emotional, and spiritual well-being. During this meditation, you will visualize the colors associated with each chakra. By sitting in a comfortable position and focusing on each chakra one by one, you can tap into the healing power of these vibrant colors.

As we begin this meditation, we can start by visualizing the root chakra, located at the base of the spine, as a vibrant red color. This color represents grounding and stability. As we breathe into this chakra, we can imagine the color red enveloping it, filling it with energy and vitality. Visualizing this color helps to activate and balance the root chakra, allowing us to feel more connected to the earth and more rooted in our physical bodies.

Moving up the body, we can then focus on the sacral chakra, which is associated with the color orange. This chakra is located just below the navel and governs our fertility, creativity, and emotions. By visualizing the color orange swirling around this area, we can stimulate our fertile and creative energy and enhance our reproductive essence. You may want to give this chakra extra time, sending love and warmth to your womb.

Next, we come to the solar plexus chakra, represented by the color yellow. This chakra is located in the upper abdomen and is responsible for our personal power and self-confidence. This chakra is also important for your digestive health. By envisioning a bright yellow light radiating from this area, we can strengthen our digestion and sense of self-worth and can increase our personal power.

Continuing up the body, we reach the heart chakra, which vibrates with the color green. This chakra is located in the center of the chest and is associated with love, compassion, and healing. By visualizing a warm green light surrounding this area, we can open ourselves up to giving and receiving love more freely and can experience a deep sense of harmony within ourselves and with others. When meditating on this chakra, you may also want to think of those you love or even send love to your womb and future baby.

Moving further up, we come to the throat chakra, represented by the color blue. This chakra governs our communication and self-expression. By visualizing a bright blue light illuminating this area, we can enhance our ability to speak our truth with clarity and authenticity.

Next, we focus on the third-eye chakra, which is associated with the color indigo. Located in the center of the forehead, this chakra is responsible for our intuition and inner wisdom. By visualizing an indigo light shining at this point, we can sharpen our intuition and connect more deeply with our inner guidance.

Finally, we reach the crown chakra, at the top of the head. This chakra is represented by the colors violet or white. It connects us to higher realms of consciousness and spiritual awareness. By envisioning a beautiful violet or white light surrounding this area and expanding beyond it, we can open ourselves up to divine guidance and experience a greater sense of spiritual connection.

By practicing this chakra-harmonizing meditation regularly and visualizing these vibrant colors, we can bring balance to our energy centers and promote healing on all levels. The colors associated with each chakra have specific vibrations that resonate with different aspects of our being. Through visualization, we can harness these vibrations and create a harmonious flow of energy within ourselves. Allow yourself to experience the healing power of these colors and embrace a greater sense of well-being and vitality.

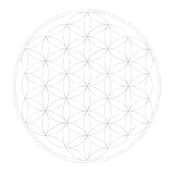

CHAPTER 11

Inviting Joy

The Essence That We Seek

So often, my patients tell me that joy has left their lives ever since they began their journeys to conceive. While it is very understandable that having fertility challenges can be a very traumatic experience, I encourage my patients to not give up on the moments that bring them joy. This is not about ignoring or invalidating their loss and sadness, but actually about feeding themselves the fuel to get through this experience. It is human nature to get hyper-focused on finding a solution and perhaps in the process ignore our own needs. A woman in this situation has to bring extra consciousness and awareness to the practice of self-care in order to help herself approach the challenges with greater clarity and personal energy.

Joy is the spirit's fuel. It doesn't need to be shelved or forced—it is something that our souls are attracted to because it is our deepest desire. Joy is our natural state and birthright. It is our minds that convince us that we can't afford to feel joy or that, if we feel joy, we may not be taking our mission seriously enough.

The power of joy not only changes one's perspective, but apparently, it has physiological effects as well. Having a positive mental state impacts the state of the heart,[1] which, as you learned in chapter 7, has a very important impact on the uterus due to the heart-uterus connection via the Bao Mai channel. A positive emotional state has also been linked with increased resistance_to colds.[2]

When you ask yourself why you really desire something, focus on the object at first. Then ask yourself why you want that object, asking again and again until you come down to one word. For example, many people who want to accomplish a goal of making money may actually be attracted to the freedom it can bring, so they are really after freedom. For others, their why could be something else. When I ask my patients why they want to have children, many of them have expressed that they want to experience the joy and reward of having another being to live for. Ultimately, most of my patients express that joy is the feeling they are seeking at the core of their desire to have a baby. But what's interesting is that they also unconsciously—or even consciously—feel that they cannot afford to feel joy until they get through their treatments or pregnancy. It seems as though joy has a condition, and they feel like they need to check a few more boxes in order to afford it.

Joy is not a goal; it is a state of mind. To think of joy as a goal takes away from the possibility of joy emerging in the present moment. This perception of joy as a goal is completely counter to what joy is. Joy is expansive and free; joy has an unconditional nature. That being said, this doesn't mean that you can't also honor your feelings of grief and sadness. These feelings can coexist. Oftentimes, people are just not aware that they are putting conditions on joy, and that is okay. The important thing is to ask yourself these questions:

- Are you afraid to feel joy before you get the object that represents joy?
- When was the last time you did something that brought you joy?
- Do you think you deserve to feel joy?
- Is joy a state that depends on a specific outcome?
- Do you think postponing joy is influencing your ability to be present?

It is important to ask yourself these types of questions because true empowerment begins with awareness. True awareness can often appear when you ask the right questions. Sometimes you can find the answers just by asking the questions—often, the questions shed light on things you may not have been ready to think about otherwise. Just remind yourself that these questions can only help you when you are ready.

Joy Is Your Fuel

It may feel like joy is not the priority when you are struggling to conceive. I would like to challenge that thought by saying that joy may actually be precisely what you need to fuel your ability to face your fertility challenges.

I see so many of my patients feeling defeated and emotionally drained. I stress to them how important their well-being is, and even though they start off looking at me sideways, they eventually understand. Seeing my patients come to a place where they are smiling and at ease well before they have accomplished their goal is one of the most rewarding aspects of my work. Reaching this place of surrender does not give them any less of a chance to accomplish their goal. Quite the opposite—it helps them attain a state of physical and emotional harmony that supports reproductive healing and, eventually, conception.

When we afford ourselves a state that we desire, we are giving ourselves a message that all is well. This impacts our sleep, our cortisol, and our hormone levels. Did you know that progesterone is also a precursor to the stress hormone cortisol? While cortisol has a necessary purpose in our bodies' stress response, chronically elevated cortisol can lower progesterone levels, impacting a woman's ability to sustain a healthy pregnancy. This is just one of many ways that stress can impact reproductive health. If stress is a ball filled with pressure, joy is the conduit through which the pressure can get released.

Finding Joy in the Unknown

By the time Nancy came to see me, she had undergone two ectopic pregnancies as well as three years of in vitro fertilization, which had included six transfers that had ended in three miscarriages. She no longer had her fallopian tubes, and IVF was her only option. She was a smoker, and she had a very hard time changing her habit and sleeping well.

Nancy saw me for over a year, during which time she implemented new habits that improved her overall health. She listened to her fertility hypnosis audios regularly and even enrolled in a yoga certification program. Over time, I began to see her transform; she began to live with more presence and an overflow of joy. She began putting her well-being first.

Nancy started to feel a sense of hope for her journey. Although she strongly desired a healthy pregnancy, she was able to experience a state of emotional freedom rather than an attachment to the outcome. After some time, she had an egg retrieval where she ended up with two healthy embryos. Although she had every reason to be scared—and she still was—Nancy maintained a state of trust and joy that was amazing to see.

Nancy transferred one of her embryos and conceived. She now has a beautiful baby girl from her successful transfer.

The Magic in Humor

Laughter is one of the quickest ways to release the pressure built up by stress.[3] Laughter has also demonstrated the ability to improve overall well-being. It has been shown to improve IVF transfer outcomes too.[4] Learning about the research is great, but we don't need proof to know that laughter and the accompanying physical release it provides have powerful effects on our mindset. When laughing, we are immersed in and fully surrendered to the moment.

Laughter is a fairly easy way to invite joy; all we need to do is watch a comedy that speaks to us. It helps to do this with someone else because laughter is contagious, and it is easier to induce when the moment is shared. The feeling that laughter provides is an immediate exhilaration and a feeling of endorphins flooding your body. It has an amazing effect of loosening the muscles and freeing up any tightness in the body.

I often recommend that couples watch comedies together! This can be another way for a couple to bond during their fertility journey and can invite a dynamic that is lighthearted and fun.

Joy and Love, the Ultimate Power Couple

Love is a powerful, life-giving emotion that is intertwined with joy. The comfort of love has the power to help people surrender and heal. It is a surrender similar to what one feels when having a blissful moment of joy; it's infused with trust and ease.

The fertility journey can be very taxing on couples as they try to navigate the loss and hurt that may come up. As we discussed in chapter 3, being given a rigid timeline for when to be intimate in order to conceive can also squash any spontaneity and cause an aversion to intimacy.

When dealing with fertility difficulties and intimacy protocols, couples can feel that their connection is becoming mechanical. I usually suggest that such couples become intimate on days outside of the fertile window. Going on dates, holding hands, eye-gazing, breathing in tandem, and dancing are just some examples of how couples can rekindle this feeling of love and, consequently, joy.

Love can be cultivated in a number of ways. Ultimately, it is up to you how you want to fill your love tank. Love will ultimately help you seek out joyful events and invite them into your life.

Self-Love, Joy, and Conception

We often think about the joy of loving others, but we rarely recognize the power, need, and joy that come from self-love. Self-love is joy in action, and it comes in handy when women are dealing with practitioners who doubt their ability to conceive.

Amie is a perfect example of someone who chose to bet on her own chances and dreams of becoming a mother, even in the face of discouraging news. When Amie came to me, she was thirty-nine years old and had been trying to conceive for over a year with no success. She had gone to the best fertility doctors in two different countries—Greece and the US. Her reproductive endocrinologist in the US said that, based on her labs and tests, she appeared to be perimenopausal (approaching menopause), had a very low egg count, and would need IVF in order to conceive. Her doctor in Greece confirmed that Amie had a very low egg count and would need IVF. He added that she would probably not be able to use her own eggs and would need to find an egg donor.

While both IVF and egg donation are great options for many people, Amie felt deep in her heart that they weren't her path. Even after two reputable reproductive endocrinologists gave her very similar assessments, Amie decided to take a more "risky" path and try natural methods to get pregnant. She came to my office and enrolled in my fertility program. She expressed to me that she felt really strongly about her body's ability to heal and return to balance. She had a palpable belief in herself that impressed me.

After working with her in person for three weeks, I was forced to shut down my clinic in response to the COVID-19 pandemic. We had to switch to working together virtually, while Amie also consistently listened to the hypnosis audios I provided and visualized her pregnancy. Even though it wasn't always easy, she began intently focusing on what brought her joy in life by infusing gratitude into everything she loved. After a few weeks, she reached out to me, very confused about her menstrual cycle changes. She was late on her period but did not get a positive pregnancy result on her test. Her doctor's use of the term "perimenopause" began to haunt her as she questioned if this unusual delay of her period signified an imbalance. She tried a few pregnancy tests, and still they came out negative. She asked me to show her acupressure points to start her period, but something inside me told me to wait. I asked her to humor me and get another pregnancy test from the store. Amie did, and she discovered she was pregnant!

Amie went on to give birth after a healthy full-term pregnancy. She breastfed for nine months, got her period, and then fell pregnant once more. Amie now has two children she brought into the world without any technical intervention, just as she knew deep in her heart she could. She had a strong sense of self-advocacy, the same advocacy and belief a mother would have around raising her children. This is self-love embodied, and this self-love is life-giving. It is faith and conviction in one's own potential, and it is powerful!

Amie shared her story on episode 208 of my podcast, and she recalled allowing herself a deep sense of joy and freedom every night when she listened to the fertility hypnosis audios I had created for her. While she had remained aware of the unknown nature of her journey, Amie still made time every evening to feed her inner joy, which gave her the fuel to keep going.[5]

Love Immersion

A powerful practice in cultivating joy is immersing yourself in a feeling of love. This may sound strange, but you can actually cultivate the feeling of love through an ancient tradition and meditation from Buddhism referred to as "loving kindness." The loving kindness practice uses a meditation called "Metta meditation," where a person wishes people well-being, starting with themselves and then their loved ones, continuing on to people they like, then people they are neutral about, and eventually even moving on to people who have hurt them. The effects of this meditation are very powerful and have been shown to increase positive emotions.[6]

Here's how to practice the loving kindness meditation.

Sit in a comfortable seated position. Inhale and exhale a few times. Become aware of any sensations you have in your body as you inhale and exhale. Settle into your body and the present moment.

Once you feel quiet, say the following things in your mind, filling the blank with "I" first, then filling the blank with your loved ones, then filling the blank with people you like, then people you are neutral toward, then people you dislike, and finally, if and when you're ready, people who you have grievances toward.

The following are examples of sentences you may use.

May (blank) be loved and nourished.

May (blank) be well and protected.

May (blank) be free of harm.

May (blank) be free of suffering.

May (blank) be healthy.

May (blank) experience peace of mind.

You can add more of these if you like. When you first start, cultivate a warm and fuzzy feeling as you wish your loved ones well. This is the energy that you are cultivating, which you want to expand out to your outer circle. You may want to start with only your inner circle at first until you are ready to wish wellness on those you dislike or you hold resentment toward. This practice should feel easy and not forced.

The Metta meditation is especially powerful for supporting the heart–uterus connection. It helps evoke feelings of connection, which are especially important for supporting what's at the heart of baby making—the union of two partners.

The Art of Play

Sometimes finding joy can look like getting lost in artwork, baking, hiking, or an amazing book that you can't put down. Playing should not be something that we outgrow; it is one of the healthiest activities you can do for your soul and body! How long has it been since you've done something you love?

Many people have the common misconception that they can only play once everything on their list gets accomplished, and as we all know, that might never happen! There is no need to create rules and conditions for taking some time for fun. Giving yourself time to be free to do things that bring out your inner child will not only help you release stress, it will also serve as a charging station during a time that can feel heavy and pressured, as is often the case during the fertility journey.

I often tell my patients that becoming a mother can start with mothering yourself. Doing so can look like allowing yourself the freedom that comes with immersing yourself in a state of play. A state of play is anything that brings you out of your analytical mind and allows for a moment of freedom and fun! It's a time to take yourself less seriously and drop all cares and concerns for a moment. Activities like going on a swing or spending a day at a theme park may even remind you of a carefree version of yourself from when you were growing up.

The amount of stress released during this time of play will surprise you! It will feel, for at least a moment, as if you have gotten permission to forget your problems and recharge your energy. This is ultimate joy; it's a relinquishment of control that feels so freeing!

Joy Is Just a Mindset Away

Although sometimes it can be a challenge, it's worth investing your time engaging in activities that invite a state of joy. The biggest challenge is overcoming that belief that you are not supposed to feel joy until you reach your goal of having your baby. In reality, it is not only possible to allow yourself joy while on the fertility journey, but the essence of joy, by its very nature, may open a portal for blessings to emerge.

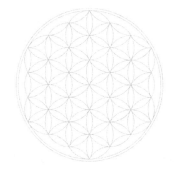

CHAPTER 12
We Were Born to Create

We Are, First and Foremost, Creative Beings

A ccording to traditional Chinese medicine, our liver ensures the free flow of qi, or life force vitality. When our liver is not focused on counteracting stress, it can allow for the freedom of qi, which ultimately allows us to be in our natural state of creativity. This subsequently allows the body to create more of its natural substances, such as qi and blood, to support fertility. Engaging in activities that are creative can also impact that sense of energetic freedom and assist the liver's role of ensuring the free flow of qi.

Even if you were given messages when you were young that you're not creative, nothing could be further from the truth! In fact, we create all the time. Sometimes we create consciously, and other times we create by default. If you weren't creative, you wouldn't be able to shift and pivot your response to new obstacles that come up in your life. You have to be creative in order to come up with solutions or ideas. As humans, we have a unique ability to be creative at all times. Our only issue is that we sometimes convince ourselves that we are more limited than we really are.

Being creative does not mean you have to be a skilled artist or musician. Those are simply methods through which to channel creativity. There are so many ways to express creativity, including through writing, dancing, singing, cooking, visualizing, painting, coloring, or organizing furniture. Creativity doesn't have to be expressed in just one way, and it doesn't have to be perfect!

Now that I've given you examples of how you are already creative, I want to propose to you that there is another layer to your ability to create: your ability to create your life itself. We, as humans, are born with an innate ability to visualize, conceptualize, and actualize. Everything you see around you, including the homes, the things you use, and the highways you drive on, all started with a vision. Not only did those objects first start with a vision, but your choice of career, marriage, or relationships began when you first thought about those things, and then later, you actualized them at future events. What you think and imagine matters.

Your thoughts don't just randomly create some things and turn into floating blobs for others. They impact everything. That doesn't mean that if you have bad thoughts, all of them will become real—at least, not necessarily. But your thoughts might hold you back from creating and actualizing what you do want. They might limit your chances of trying by limiting your belief in the outcome. However you want to look at it—and it can certainly be looked at in endless different ways—your thoughts impact your life, and they can impact your reproductive outcomes in particular because your thoughts are the directors of your life's creative potential.

Most of Us Create Whether We Want to or Not—Why It's Important to Release before Planting Seeds

When you use your innate ability to create from a place of intention, the whole world opens up to you. This describes conscious creation, an often-untapped power that tends to not be used to its potential.

Approaching life with intention is the antithesis of reacting to life by default, which is what many of us unknowingly do. This is not to say that we should completely dismiss what we have been told by professionals or what we have experienced on the journey. Instead, we should bring in an element of proactivity and lay a foundation of our highest vision as we invite the growth of our family.

Many people don't do this, and not because they are completely unaware of the power of envisioning, but because it can be scary to allow ourselves to dream. Many of us had experiences growing up when we allowed ourselves to visualize an outcome, only to have it crushed when things didn't turn out as expected. This is where the element of flow comes in handy. Instead of seeing our reality as one that should be controlled, we can see it as a dance of co-creation where all parts unite to assist in the outcome. It's about acknowledging our dream and not allowing disappointments to dictate how we move forward.

Creating consciously starts with awareness, becoming mindful of your daily thoughts and taking responsibility for the role you play in your life's creations. This does not mean feeling blame or shame. Instead, it means simply observing with objectivity rather than feeling bias and overanalyzing. Once you get a clear picture of what's occurring in your inner terrain, you can allow yourself the leisure of deciding what you would like to create for your life. This means dropping the "how" and simply focusing on the end vision of what you would like to bring into your life. Focusing in too much depth on the "how" can invite thoughts that your vision won't work or isn't realistic. The "how" can also be a creativity crusher. Instead, simply allow yourself the freedom to dream up your desired outcome of not only growing your family but having your highest desires come true.

Second Chakra Energy—Why Creativity Supports Fertility and Requires Trust

The energy of creativity dwells in our sacral chakra, which is our second chakra. This chakra rests on the root chakra, which means that we need to feel grounded and safe in order to create. When people don't feel safe, they don't create. This is why fear of failure or judgment can act as the biggest blocks for artists of all kinds. This is what causes many children to get an early creativity block when they receive messages that they're drawing outside of the lines or are not creating "right."

All of us start out creative as children, but eventually, some of us begin to believe we are not creative. I personally believe we are all meant to create. What's more, creativity is the energetic aspect of fertility. We conceive in our minds and give birth to our ideas, inventions, or creations through our choice to take action on those conceptions.

In order to create, however, there needs to be a feeling of freedom and safety. It's kind of similar to a physical orgasm— and no, this isn't unrelated! Orgasm and sexual energy both dwell in the creative center of the second chakra. When that chakra is open, we feel an opening and freedom of sexual and creative expression. But, as I mentioned in chapter 10, chakras are interdependent and need each other in order to be balanced. They are not islands, but part of a greater whole.

The biggest question you can ask yourself when it comes to the foundation of your creative center (your root chakra) is whether you feel safe. If you find that you don't feel safe, ask yourself why, and note when these unsafe feelings come up. Not only is it important to be aware, but you can also affirm your safety by simply repeating, "I am safe" throughout the day. Even if you don't believe the words of this affirmation at first, keep repeating it until it makes its way into your subconscious mind.

A quote by Deepak Chopra underscores the importance of safety in supporting creativity. He said, "The best use of imagination is creativity. The worst use of imagination is anxiety."[1] In simple terms, creativity breathes life, and chronic fear depletes vitality. The problem is that during the fertility journey, couples get messages that are based in rigid predictions that, many times, sound hopeless. These predictions naturally bring them away from a state of spaciousness, safety, and creativity while discouraging them from imagining desirable outcomes. It is important to be proactive about cultivating a state of creativity so that you don't slip into a mode of reactivity rather than a state of proactivity.

One of the ways you can evoke a state of creativity is by doing things that inspire creative flow such as dancing, listening to music, doodling, using your less dominant hand, visualizing, singing, or cooking. Let's go over a few ways to use your innate creativity to not only ease any anxiety but open yourself up energetically to your reproductive energy center.

Neurographic Art

Neurographic art is an innovative form of art therapy that heals the mind and helps individuals cope with various challenges. The technique was developed by Russian artist Pavel Piskarev, who combined his knowledge of psychology and art to create a method that engages both the left and right hemispheres of the brain. This bilateral activation promotes relaxation and stimulates creative thinking, allowing individuals to express their emotions and thoughts in a visual form.

For women going through the emotional roller coaster of trying to conceive, neurographic art can serve as a creative outlet and a means to find solace and calm, especially during stressful moments such as the "two-week wait" period.

Creating neurographic art is a simple yet powerful process. It involves using repetitive patterns and lines to create unique and intricate designs.

To create neurographic art, all you need is a plain piece of paper, a pen or marker, and an open mind. Start by drawing a simple shape or outline on the paper, and then begin to fill the paper with continuous lines, loops, and swirls. The goal is to let your hand move freely, without any preconceived ideas or expectations. Then soften the "Xs" where you see lines cross, connecting the right angles with curved lines and then filling in those lines. It might help to watch a video on this; you can find instructional video resources linked here: https://www.michelle oravitz.com/thewayoffertilityresources.

As you continue drawing, you may start to notice that your mind enters a state of flow where you become fully absorbed in the creative process. This state of focused attention can bring about a sense of calm and tranquility, providing relief from the anxiety and stress associated with the fertility journey.

Neurographic art has the power to transform the mind in various ways. It allows those on the fertility journey to channel their emotions and thoughts into a tangible form of expression. By visually representing your experiences and feelings through art, you can gain a sense of control over your emotions and find release from the intense pressure you may be experiencing. Neurographic art also activates both the analytical and creative parts of the brain, stimulating cognitive flexibility and problem-solving skills. This can be particularly helpful when one is faced with fertility challenges and difficult decisions, as it can open up a different perspective and exploration of new possibilities.

Remember that you do not have to be a skilled artist to try neurographic art, and it's another method of allowing the mind to release tension and get into a creative flow. You can try neurographic art while listening to your favorite music, and you can even diffuse your favorite essential oils to create a creative, calm sensory experience.

Visualizations

Creative visualizations have an incredible power to impact not only your reproductive potential but also your overall biology. Our minds don't distinguish between real or imagined experiences. This means that when we engage in creative visualizations, our minds believe that what we are imagining is actually happening. This is why visualizations can be so powerful in shaping our reality and influencing our biology.

Studies conducted on the benefits of creative visualization have yielded promising results. For example, research has shown that visualizing a desired outcome can enhance performance in sports and other competitive activities.[2] Athletes who consistently incorporate visualizations into their training routines have been found to experience improved focus, confidence, and overall performance. Similarly, individuals can create a mental state that is conducive to conception by using regular visualizations.

One reason visualizations are so effective is because they allow us to tap into the power of our subconscious mind. Our subconscious mind controls our beliefs, emotions, and behaviors. By using creative visualizations, we can directly access and reprogram our subconscious mind, which in turn influences our biology. This means that, by consistently engaging in positive visualizations, we can actually rewire our brains and create new neural pathways that support our desired outcomes.

Another interesting aspect of visualizations is that they can activate the mind–body connection. This means that when we visualize ourselves as healthy, fertile, and vibrant, our bodies respond by releasing feel-good hormones and activating healing processes. This mind–body connection further enhances the power of creative visualizations and their impact on our reproductive potential and overall biology.

We can use our creativity in so many ways, and creative visualizations are just one example of a way to use creativity as a powerful tool that can positively impact our reproductive potential and biology. By consistently using creative visualizations, you can wire your brain to get better at visualizing and direct it to tap into your reproductive potential.

If you find that visualizing is hard and you are more audial or relate more to words, you can start by describing what you're imagining until visualizing becomes easier for your mind to do. You can also start by bringing up a positive memory and seeing the colors and scenes in your mind's eye. The more you practice, the more natural visualization becomes!

Using Writing to Create

Our thoughts and beliefs can shape our reality, and writing down our goals is a powerful way to harness this power. When we write down our goals, we are sending a clear message to our subconscious mind about what we want to manifest in our lives. A study conducted by a professor at the Dominican University of California has shown that writing down your goals can actually increase the chances that they will actualize.[3]_By simply putting pen to paper and expressing your desires, you are setting in motion a series of events that can impact the manifestation of your goals. This study highlights the power of writing and its influence on our subconscious mind.

By writing in the present tense, we are affirming that our goals are not just dreams for the future, but possibilities that can be realized in the present moment. When it comes to starting a family and improving fertility health, most of the time, people use the words "want" or "will happen," which can indicate that our goals are out of our reach and will always be in the future. By writing down your desire to start a family in the present tense, you are telling your subconscious mind that this is not just a future goal, but something that is happening right now. This sends a powerful message to your mind and body, aligning them with your intention and increasing your chances of manifesting your desires.

Writing in the present tense has a profound impact on our subconscious mind. When we write our goals as if they have already been achieved, our subconscious mind accepts this as truth and begins to work toward making it a reality. It's like programming a GPS—it immediately starts guiding you toward the point you entered as your destination. Similarly, when you write down your goals as if they have already happened, your subconscious mind starts guiding you toward making them a reality.

Writing in the present tense also helps to cultivate a positive mindset. By focusing on what you want to achieve and expressing it in the present tense, you are training your mind to believe in the possibility that your dreams will come true. This is why starting a gratitude journal can be so impactful as well—because you're creating a habit of focusing on things that empower you. This ultimately provides a source of personal energy, which, as we know, is vital for reproductive health!

Secrets to Manifesting

Our biggest block to manifesting is our identification with a limited version of ourselves. I say "version" because we always have a choice for how we want to live out our expression, which means all expressions are versions of ourselves that we have chosen to communicate. We simply don't realize that we are able to tap into a boundless potential that awaits our discovery.

How do I know this? Because once I discovered how to manifest, I was able to create very specific instances in my life. Those specific signs were my confirmation of the power of my creation. I did this with my marriage, with my house, and with my career, and I am now teaching my clients to do it as well. If you only knew how much potential power you possessed, you would tap into it much more.

But, as I mentioned earlier in the chapter, we manifest whether we mean to or not—when it's unconscious, we don't always manifest what we want. My personal belief is that, if you have a strong desire to do something, anything, then that is a call from a potential outcome to be brought forth and manifested. That desire is not random; something deep within is calling you to bring it to life. If you are questioning your intuition and your abilities, then ask for guidance and signs. It's really that simple. If your desire isn't manifested right away, don't be discouraged and decide it's not working, because that may block your efforts. If you are not used to connecting to your higher self in this way, the first seed you plant may take longer to sprout; be patient. I promise that if you keep feeding it with your faith in the process, you are bound to get a very strong, definitive sign that it's working.

You can begin with affirmations, writing down daily that you are guided and given signs to point you into alignment with your highest self and intuition. You can also write that you know how to actualize your deepest desires. These approaches are a great way to set a foundation. If this all seems too foreign to you, then ease yourself into some of the exercises shared in this chapter. It is important to note that you may find that some exercises feel more comfortable for you than others. If so, use what speaks best to you, as we all have our own power methods and personal language! Keep in mind that the most challenging aspect of manifesting is that, at least for a brief moment, we need to have greater faith in our dreams than in our current reality.

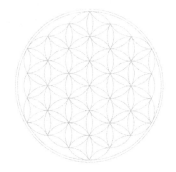

CHAPTER 13
Surrendering the Blueprint of Our Plan

Knowing the Difference between What You Can and Cannot Control

When an outcome is within our control, then resistance can be appropriate. But if nothing can be done about a certain outcome, then resistance only leads to depletion. Resisting requires more energy than most people can afford to spend, especially when they are trying to harness their energy for conception. In situations like these, surrender may be the best way forward.

Being in a state of surrender does not mean giving up our power. In fact, being in a state of surrender can be one of the most empowering things you can do in your life. Surrender can be one of the best ways to access a state of flow in your life, since pushing away what we have but don't want or grasping on to what we want but don't have can bring about disharmony and pull us out of alignment.

Choosing to surrender doesn't mean that you can't experience your pain and validate your experience. In fact, in order to process your emotions, you'll need to surrender to the existence of those emotions so they can move through you and show you the way to alignment on your journey.

Being in acceptance describes a state of Tao in which one trusts in the intelligent fabric of our reality. It's exerting energy when needed, yet also allowing oneself to be moved by an external force without resistance when that is needed. It's simply knowing when to exert and when to allow so that being in a state of surrender is not being idle, but more like moving in flow.

In some cases, couples can find themselves hitting walls at every turn they take. I've seen couples go through years on end of IVF fertility treatments with no success, then get pregnant once they pause and try naturally. In other cases, couples may need a donor egg, donor sperm, donor embryo, or even adoption. I personally believe that if couples are called to start a family or want to grow their existing family, this calling is real. Sometimes, however, things don't pan out the exact way we envision them, and this is when it's important to become receptive and accept the divine guidance you receive on the journey to your child. This can look like pivoting plans or rethinking an approach when the same action for many years hasn't yielded the hoped-for result of conceiving your child.

Guided by Her Fertility Journey

Nancy Weiss is an intuitive fertility coach who shared her amazing story on episode 152 of my podcast.

Nancy and her husband struggled to conceive for over two years until one day, they learned about embryo donors. Nancy felt an immediate pull to the idea of taking this route to parenthood.

Interestingly, Nancy and her husband had moved to Georgia a few years before she decided to look for embryo donors. She describes her decision to move as something that felt completely random at the time. Their only reason for making this life choice had been that they felt called to move! Little did she know that her two sister embryos, who would have been teens if they had been transferred right after they were formed, were waiting for her in Georgia.[1]

Nancy's story has inspired countless podcast listeners. I've had so many of them reach out to me to let me know how moved they were! What I love about Nancy's story is that, being an intuitive, she was already open to the potential magic that existed in the universe. She allowed herself to be led to a path that she hadn't originally anticipated for herself and her husband. Because of her openness, she is now a mother to two beautiful girls, and she would do it all again in a heartbeat!

Why Relinquishing Control Gives You More Power (Even Though It Feels like the Opposite Is True)

Have you ever played catch or any other sport that required an instinctual response? You may have noticed that, when you overthink it and get in your own way, it can cause you to miss or underperform. The same applies when taking tests, having interviews, making friends, and so on. When you overthink and try to control something too much, it can get in the way of the natural flow of events. I personally know this to be true when I'm painting. The more I try to control how things go, the more it impedes my creative flow. Sometimes we think that we need to control an outcome in order for it to produce the results we are looking for, but this may not be the best approach.

Exerting too much control is not the same as setting an intention. Setting an intention is bringing forth, with clarity, what we are hoping to accomplish in any given endeavor. When you set an intention while also relinquishing control and letting the pieces fall where they need to, you are allowing for universal intelligence to work for you. This can only happen when we get out of our own way while also being clear on our intention. Balancing these two concepts is another form of using effort while also allowing, as discussed in previous chapters. Choosing to over-control is not choosing strength. It is choosing to assume that everything falls on your shoulders alone and ignoring one of the gifts we have as humans, which is our access to universal intelligence.

Access to universal intelligence can only be felt with experience. If someone tells you of their experience, then it may or may not move you, and for it to do so requires complete trust in the story you are told. You have access to your own miracles, but that access can only be experienced with some amount of faith. Your belief in universal intelligence is the bridge that connects you with its powers. I know this because of my own experiences, which only came to fruition when I opened up to the potential of universal intelligence being real. You can do this too if you choose to allow universal intelligence to actualize miracles in your life through your belief in them. Once you become aware and acknowledge that you are connected to a higher source that you can rely on, miracles will show up in ways you never expected. You will find a wealth of sweet surprises. This comes with a faith and a knowing that you already have all you need.

Getting into a State of Allowing

Our modern lifestyle conditions us to believe that we need to exert active effort if we want anything in life. While this certainly comes in handy and can be very necessary, exerting active effort is a very yang state of being, and it requires balance in order to remain effective. Sometimes we need to be in a state of receptivity in order to get what we want, but it may not be easy for us to transition into a state that is counter to our conditioning.

One of the best ways to get into a state of receiving is through meditation or stillness. When we are quiet, we increase our awareness, our inner state of listening. A state of listening, by nature, is one that receives.

As mentioned in chapter 4, the human egg is a beautiful example of the ultimate yin or feminine state of receiving. To fulfill its purpose, the egg attracts with its sound; it does not seek. If it went against its nature, it would work against itself. We can learn a great deal from the egg's behavior and how it can do so much while being so subtle in its activity. The first instinct we have as humans is to do more when we are met with resistance, but sometimes it's more powerful to do less.

The reality is that there is no perfect way to do anything. It always comes down to balance and flow. This requires both effort and effortlessness, depending on what every moment needs. A state of allowing is one of surrender, where we pause in our efforts in order to not only receive what we desire but also be guided toward our highest and greatest good. This is when alignment can take place, which is ultimately the best possible outcome for us, regardless of any shortsighted expectations we may have about what we "should" have. Allowing creates space for the bigger picture to emerge, one that we don't always have a conscious perspective on.

A state of allowing is a state of trust. A state of trust is a state of knowing that we are safe and of believing that we are being guided by a higher intelligence. The story of Nancy Weiss, the intuitive fertility coach, truly demonstrates this. When she went into a state of allowing, she was guided to her two sister embryos in Georgia, who she knew in her heart had been hers all along. This story is truly miraculous, and miracles sprout when they have an abundance of trust.

Flower vs. the Bee—A State of Mind

There are two main ways to acquire what we want. One of the ways is to go after it directly. The other is to invite it or call it in. You can look at these as a yin and yang approach of receiving. One is exerting effort, and the other is attracting.

The flower and the bee make a beautiful example of this. They have a symbiotic relationship where both parties benefit. Their approaches in making the relationship happen, however, are opposite. The bee takes a yang approach and seeks out the flower to pollinate. The flower, in yin form, simply exudes its scent so that the bee can find it.

For humans, there is no clear-cut right or wrong approach, but if you are continuously hitting walls, you may benefit from considering a different approach. One of the best signs that you are aligned in your efforts is that those efforts are moving the needle. This is where you get into that state of flow, which does not mean a state of no effort, but that the effort is productive rather than consistently draining you and providing no result.

Most of the time, what I observe when I first speak to new patients is that they have worked overtime to try to conceive. This is completely understandable, and, in all honesty, I would probably do the same thing! This can be extremely draining and frustrating to no end. That is why I try to shift the efforts to also include more yin activities that bring them into a state of receptivity and rest.

When I went to my first weeklong retreat with Dr. Joe Dispenza, he explained the difference between approaching reality from a material form (Newtonian physics) and a wavelength approach (quantum physics). When we identify with a more dense material form, we have to exert more effort to go from A to C. But when we get into what Dr. Dispenza calls the field of potentiality, we take our attention away from the path to get there and simply act as a magnet, inviting the outcome to us.

I have personally seen the effect that this change has had in my life, and I'm lucky enough to get to observe countless patients' different approaches and witness miracles happening when they start to align themselves to what I can best refer to as "quantum fertility."

The Power of Surrender

There is power in surrender. It is a state that is imbued with a feeling of trust, brought to life by some sense of faith in the divine intelligence that runs our life. Dr. Lisa Miller, the *New York Times* best-selling author of *The Spiritual Child* and *The Awakened Brain*, was a guest on episode 232 of my podcast, and she shared about the role surrender played in her personal journey of starting her family. I found her through a TEDx talk she held about her fertility journey, which eventually led her to her adopted son.

Dr. Miller and her husband struggled to conceive for many years, both naturally and through IVF. She found herself unable to get anywhere with her efforts, and this sent her into a deep depression. On my podcast, she shared her story of finding a duck embryo on her doorstep and, later that night, getting a knock on her window from the mother duck. These were some of the strange signs she received when she simply didn't know how to navigate her yearning to become a mother. She also shared an interesting voice she heard in her mind, both early on and on another occasion, asking her whether she would adopt if she got pregnant naturally. Her answer at the time was no.

One day, she saw a program on TV showing an orphan being interviewed. What's interesting is that the TV didn't allow her to change the channel. During the interview, the orphan told the interviewer that "it hurts so much *to not be* loved that I sniff glue to make the pain go away." This hit Dr. Miller and her husband on such a primal level that they began looking into adoption immediately. When they found their boy (she immediately knew him when she saw his picture!) and she was preparing the night before her flight to pick him up, she heard that voice again. "If you conceived naturally, would you still adopt?" Her answer was an unequivocal "Yes!" Shortly thereafter, she conceived her son's sister.[2]

Dr. Miller's story gives me goosebumps to this day! Her story is one of the universe trying to draw her attention to a calling that was different from what she had planned. Her book *The Awakened Brain*, which was written to share much of her research in the field of psychology, shares studies confirming the power that spirituality has on the brain. Her research uncovers the impact that believing in a higher power has on the physical brain. Believing in a higher power or divine intelligence actually protects believers from experiencing depression!

You Are Enough

One of the biggest challenges on the fertility journey is knowing that, despite your difficulties conceiving, you are enough. It is so easy to judge ourselves when our bodies don't produce the outcome we expect. Part of surrendering our plans also comes with accepting ourselves in our entirety.

This is not to say that it's not normal to have moments of frustration, as we are, after all, human. But it's also important to give ourselves grace and space to navigate the often-challenging journey to conception.

I often suggest to my patients that they allow themselves a break from time to time. This allows them mental and emotional space to find what it was that gave them joy before they embarked on this journey. It also allows for their identification with their condition to loosen its grip so that they can feel more whole and aligned with themselves. What I often find happens is that, as a side effect, taking a break often results in pregnancy. This is because, when you nourish your well-being, you also create an opportunity for balance and healing to take place. Taking a break eases pressure and creates the flow dynamic that I spoke about in earlier chapters.

When you realize you're enough, you become aware of your innate wholeness. You can then see that what you consider a weakness, like moments of difficulty, is still valid and has a place in your life. Getting to a place of completely accepting yourself in your entirety is a potent step toward empowerment. This can take some time to embrace, but ultimately, it's a path to healing your body and mind.

Here are some affirmations you can repeat or write down if you find yourself stuck in a pattern of self-criticism or are even feeling resentment toward your journey.

- I am enough just as I am.
- I love and accept my body in its entirety.
- My body aligns effortlessly to prepare for a healthy conception.
- Universal intelligence is always working to help me on my journey.
- Every day, in every way, I find ease and flow as my body heals.

These examples can be a great starting point for writing your own affirmations. When you repeat these phrases over and over again, it will have an impact on your well-being. This is just one tool to help you get to a harmonious state of flow, which ultimately helps your body regulate and heal any imbalances. You can also scan your body and repeat in your mind, "I love you" to each area that feels tense, or you can focus love toward your reproductive organs. This may sound super simplistic, but don't underestimate the power of using your intention in this way. The great thing about it is that, whether you believe in it or not, there's nothing to lose in trying!

The Art of Allowing

As the title to this section says, allowing is an art. It does not happen overnight. You shouldn't have to force a state of allowing or trust; it is something that naturally happens when you get your mind and body in a state of ease and well-being. These are states that are not meant to be saved until a particular event happens; these are states that you deserve to experience often.

The best way to approach a state of allowing is by first becoming aware of your resistance—without judgment, without editing. Just observe it. Remember, your awareness in and of itself is imbued with intelligent life force. Just your awareness itself is enough to regulate and harmonize that which it watches *objectively and without judgment*. I call that "pure awareness" because, when there are judgment and identifications, they change the integrity of the awareness.

Having judgment and identifications with our awareness is not always bad. Judgment and identifications can be used to our advantage when we use them to work toward what we want and don't want. But in this case, there is some benefit to getting into what can be looked at as homeostasis awareness, where our current naturally defaults to our original state of magic by means of our neutral awareness. This is where healing can take place, as we are moving ourselves out of the way and *allowing* this intelligence to take form and help us attain harmony that is conducive to healing.

A beautiful practice you can do when you feel difficult emotions of resistance emerging or after a particularly challenging day is something most people would avoid, which is sitting with those feelings. Look at these internal resistant moments as an opportunity to digest these discomforts rather than "shelving" them, which is what happens when we don't want to feel them. Leaning into difficult tension, whether it's emotional or physical, allows for the energetic body to clear itself. This is a version of what happens with therapies such as acupuncture, but there are many ways to approach this, and one of them is using your superpower—awareness.

When you sit with these sensations, begin noticing if your mind repeats the circumstance or feeling that is causing the resistance. This is a pattern that the mind tends to take, as it has a tendency to cycle. Pay attention to any story that your mind is telling you about that circumstance. Is the mind's narrative based in absolute truth? Then begin to move your awareness from the story and into your body's response to this state of emotion. What is your body feeling? Where is it feeling it? Can you find pockets of tension? What does your breath feel like? Observe all of your sensations. You may want to move your focus from your body sensations to your breath and back with ease. You may also notice that your story emerges and your awareness wants to move back to the mind. If so, slowly bring your awareness back to your body sensations and breath.

This is a powerful exercise that will help you master your current state. It will naturally help you get into your innate state of allowing. You might also notice that, if you practice it consistently, you will be less reactive to triggers and will start to feel more empowered and clear-minded in difficult situations.

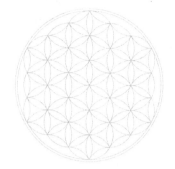

CONCLUSION
Moving Forward

Once you understand that we are an extension of nature, you see how it becomes vital that we honor this vital relationship we have with our innate home. When we treat both nature and our bodies with reverence and respect by listening to our bodies' needs and nurturing all aspects of their being, they naturally self-regulate, and this always reflects in fertility health and well-being.

By doing this, we naturally align in accordance with Tao.

Many couples approach me asking if I can treat their fertility, but I want to underscore that, in order to get to fertility, one needs to first address not only their body's health, but all aspects that create the whole of their essence. Doing so incorpo-

.rates an understanding that we thrive by respecting the laws of nature within and as an extension of our bodies.

I also want to restate this truth: there are many paths to starting or continuing a family, and there is no right or wrong way to do this! You may have had an idea or plan for how you'd prefer your fertility journey to unfold, but as we have covered in detail, life is often a dance that combines our will and the will of the intelligent soup that we are part of. At times, we may resist this dance and want to take control, but by doing this, we may unintentionally be disempowering ourselves. When we recognize the magic that happens when we decide to invite the universal intelligence into our lives, we emerge with a newfound ease as we allow ourselves to receive help and guidance from a source that knows us all too well.

Your attention combined with emotion is some of the most potent life-giving fuel imaginable. The study of quantum physics reveals that our awareness can impact a wave, becoming a particle. Our awareness has power, and it is oftentimes not used consciously in accordance with its potential. This is why I encourage you to check in with yourself regularly and get crystal clear on your intention for yourself and your growing family. Check in with any doubts that come up as well as the dreams you feel called toward.

This applies to you as a whole, in every aspect of your life. Remember, the whole of you impacts all parts of you, including your ability to conceive. We are multidimensional, interconnected, complex, brilliant beings of art. Honoring yourself as a sacred being that holds seeds of magic is the best way to open yourself up to the potential for magical blessings in your life. Allowing yourself to envision what you want for yourself is a powerful expression of self-love.

You deserve to have all your dreams come true. Know that if you feel a deep longing to start or grow your family, this is not just a coincidence. It is an invitation to explore this silent and powerful call into your fertility journey. Allow this path to guide you as you listen to its cues. By providing yourself those moments of silence and going within often, as well as following the exercises provided in this book, you are allowing yourself to connect to the highest wisdom within that has been patiently waiting to be awakened.

ACKNOWLEDGMENTS

Thank you to the beautiful fertility community I've been honored to serve, both in person and online. You have played a huge role in the inspiration for this book, and many of your stories will inspire so many who read them.

To my husband and our beautiful girls, you are my everything. Thank you to my mother, who ages like fine wine and always lights up a room; you always inspired me to reach for the stars! To my father, who I know is watching over us, you will forever live in my heart.

Thank you to all my mentors: Aimee Raupp, you probably underestimate just how much you have inspired me, and your support has truly enhanced my approach toward my patients! Dr. Deanna Minich, you truly embody Goddess energy and have such a creative, magical approach to nutrition; you are such an inspiration, and I truly appreciate all the support you have shown me! Dr. Lisa Miller, your work and your personal story are transformative! You are someone who I am so lucky to have met! And Rosanne Austin—my Joe Dispenza retreat buddy! I adore you. You have inspired me in so many ways to own my magic! You also introduced me to the next person in line, my editor and book coach, Yna Davis! Yna! Where do I begin? You literally showed me the way to my voice and made this journey so much easier than it would have been had we not met! You are truly brilliant, and I am so thankful for every part you took in this process with me!

NOTES

2. Awareness Is Your Superpower

1. Ying Sun et al., "Alteration of Faecal Microbiota Balance Related to Long-Term Deep Meditation," *General Psychiatry* 36, no. 1 (2023): e100893, https://doi.org/10.1136/gpsych-2022-100893.
2. Manoj K. Bhasin, "Specific Transcriptome Changes Associated with Blood Pressure Reduction in Hypertensive Patients after Relaxation Response Training," *Journal of Alternative and Complementary Medicine* 24, no. 5 (2018): 486–504, https://doi.org/10.1089/acm.2017.0053.
3. Cynthia J. Price and Carole Hooven, "Interoceptive Awareness Skills for Emotion Regulation: Theory and Approach of Mindful Awareness in Body-Oriented Therapy (MABT)," *Frontiers in Psychology* 9 (2018): 798, https://doi.org/10.3389/fpsyg.2018.00798.

3. Love and the Fertility Archetype

1. Sabine Wilms, *Chinese Medicine in Fertility Disorders* (Dannenberg, Germany: Thieme, 2009), 14–17.
2. Hanson et al., "Early Stress Is Associated with Alterations in the Orbitofrontal Cortex: A Tensor-Based Morphometry Investigation of Brain Structure and Behavioral Risk," *The Journal of Neuroscience: The Official Journal of the Society for Neuroscience* 30, no. 22 (2010): 7466–72, https://doi.org/10.1523/JNEUROSCI.0859-10.2010.
3. Sheau-Huey Chiu and Gene Cranston Anderson, "Effect of Early Skin-to-Skin Contact on Mother-Preterm Infant Interaction through 18 Months: Randomized Controlled Trial," *International Journal of Nursing Studies* 46, no. 9 (2009): 1168–80, https://doi.org/10.1016/j.ijnurstu.2009.03.005.
4. C. Casper, Iryna Sarapuk, and Halyna Pavlyshyn, "Regular and Prolonged Skin-to-Skin Contact Improves Short-Term Outcomes for Very Preterm Infants: A Dose-Dependent Intervention," *Archives de Pédiatrie: Organe Officiel de la Société Française de Pédiatrie* 25, no. 8 (2018): 469–75, https://doi.org/10.1016/j.arcped.2018.09.008.
5. Yoichi Chida and Andrew Steptoe, "The Association of Anger and Hostility with Future Coronary Heart Disease: A Meta-Analytic Review of Prospective Evidence," *Journal of the American College of Cardiology* 53, no. 11 (2009): 936–46, https://doi.org/10.1016/j.jacc.2008.11.044.
6. Noah J. Webster, Kristine J. Ajrouch, and Toni C. Antonucci, "Towards Positive Aging: Links between Forgiveness and Health," *OBM Geriatrics* 4, no. 2

(2021), https://doi.org/10.21926/obm.geriatr.2002118.

7. Chunyi Lin, "#71 Qigong Babies? Qigong Master Chunyi Lin Shares His Inspiring Message on the Profound Healing that Arises from Qigong," interview by Michelle Oravitz, March 17, 2020, in *The Wholesome Fertility Podcast*, podcast, MP3 audio, 1:02:19, https://www.thewholesomelotusfertility.com/thewholesomefertilitypodcast/71.

8. Allie, "#119 A Fertility Story of Hope!," interview by Michelle Oravitz, February 16, 2021, in *The Wholesome Fertility Podcast*, podcast, MP3 audio, 40:11, https://www.thewholesomelotusfertility.com/thewholesomefertilitypodcast/119.

4. The Wisdom of Yin and Yang

1. Please note that I don't necessarily recommend this supplement for all cases of a short luteal phase, as it isn't appropriate for everyone. If you're thinking of trying it, please consult with a healthcare provider first to make sure it's right for you.

5. Following the Mother Ship

1. Hyunju Jo, Chorong Song, and Yoshifumi Miyazaki, "Physiological Benefits of Viewing Nature: A Systematic Review of Indoor Experiments," *International Journal of Environmental Research and Public Health* 16, no. 23 (2019): 4739, https://doi.org/10.3390/ijerph16234739.

2. T. Reilly and I. C. Stevenson, "An Investigation of the Effects of Negative Air Ions on Responses to Submaximal Exercise at Different Times of Day," *Journal of Human Ergology* 22, no. 1 (1993): 1–9.

3. L. H. Hawkins, "The Influence of Air Ions, Temperature and Humidity on Subjective Wellbeing and Comfort," *Journal of Environmental Psychology* 1, no. 4 (1981): 279–92, https://doi.org/10.1016/S0272-4944(81)80026-6.

4. Satoko Suzuki et al., "Effects of Negative Air Ions on Activity of Neural Substrates Involved in Autonomic Regulation in Rats," *International Journal of Biometeorology* 52, no. 6 (2008): 481–9, https://doi.org/10.1007/s00484-007-0143-2.

5. Vanessa Perez, Dominik D. Alexander, and William H. Bailey, "Air Ions and Mood Outcomes: A Review and Meta-Analysis," *BMC Psychiatry* 13, no. 29 (2013), https://doi.org/10.1186/1471-244X-13-29.

6. Jenny Q. Ouyang, Scott Davies, and Davide Dominoni, "Hormonally Mediated Effects of Artificial Light at Night on Behavior and Fitness: Linking Endocrine Mechanisms with Function," *The Journal of Experimental Biology* 221, no. 6 (2018), https://doi.org/10.1242/jeb.156893.

7. Fiona C. Baker and Helen S. Driver, "Circadian Rhythms, Sleep, and the Menstrual Cycle," *Sleep Medicine* 8, no. 6, (2007): 613–22, https://doi.org/10.1016/j.sleep.2006.09.011.

8. Joshua J. Gooley et al., "Exposure to Room Light before Bedtime Suppresses Melatonin Onset and Shortens Melatonin Duration in Humans," *The Journal of Clinical Endocrinology and Metabolism* 96, no. 3 (2011): E463–72, https://doi.org/10.1210/jc.2010-2098.

9. Myung Chan Gye and Chan Jin Park, "Effect of Electromagnetic Field Exposure on the Reproductive System," *Clinical and Experimental Reproductive Medicine* 39, no. 1 (2012), 1–9, https://doi.org/10.5653/cerm.2012.39.1.1.

10. Kavindra Kumar Kesari, Ashok Agarwal, and Ralf Henkel, "Radiations and Male Fertility," *Reproductive Biology and Endocrinology* 16, no. 118 (2018), https://doi.org/10.1186/s12958-018-0431-1.

11. You-Qiong Xu, Bao-Hua Li, and Huai-Min Cheng, "High-Frequency Electromagnetic Field Exposure on Reproductive and Endocrine Functions of Female Workers," *Chinese Journal of Industrial Hygiene and Occupational Diseases* 26, no. 6 (2008): 332–5, https://pubmed.ncbi.nlm.nih.gov/18771615/.

12. Masumeh Ghazanfarpour et al., "Effect of Electromagnetic Field on Abortion: A Systematic Review and Meta-Analysis," *Open Medicine* 16, no. 1 (2021): 1628–41, https://doi.org/10.1515/med-2021-0384.

13. Maya Jammoul and Nada Lawand, "Melatonin: A Potential Shield against Electromagnetic Waves," *Current Neuropharmacology* 20, no. 3 (2022): 648–60, https://doi.org/10.2174/1570159X19666210609163946.

14. S. P. Kurotchenko et al., "Shielding Effect of Mineral Schungite during Electromagnetic Irradiation of Rats," *Bulletin of Experimental Biology and Medicine* 136, no. 5 (2003): 458–9, https://doi.org/10.1023/b:bebm.0000017092.52535.f8.

15. Heather Patisaul, ed., "Hormones and Endocrine Disrupting Chemicals: What You Need to Know," Endocrine Society, accessed December 9, 2023, https://www.endocrine.org/-/media/endocrine/files/patient-engagement/hormones-and-series/hormones_and_edcs_what_you_need_to_-know.pdf.

16. Rosa Lauretta et al., "Endocrine Disrupting Chemicals: Effects on Endocrine Glands," *Frontiers in Endocrinology* 10 (2019), https://doi.org/10.3389/fendo.2019.00178.

17. "Endocrine Disruptors," National Institute of Environmental Health Sciences, accessed January 3, 2023, https://www.niehs.nih.gov/health/topics/agents/endocrine.

18. "Research on Endocrine Disruptors," United States Environmental Protection Agency, last modified July 11, 2023, https://www.epa.gov/chemical-research/research-endocrine-disruptors.

19. Scott Zimmerman and Russel J. Reiter, "Melatonin and the Optics of the Human Body," *Melatonin Research* 2, no. 1 (Feb. 2019): 138–60, https://doi.org/https://doi.org/10.32794/mr11250016.

20. Dun-Xian Tan et al., "Melatonin: A Mitochondrial Targeting Molecule Involving Mitochondrial Protection and Dynamics," *International Journal of Molecular Sciences* 17, no. 12 (2016): 2124, https://doi.org/10.3390/ijms17122124.

21. Konstantin V. Danilenko, Oksana Y. Sergeeva, and Evgeniy G. Verevkin, "Menstrual Cycles Are Influenced by Sunshine," *Gynecological Endocrinology* 27, no. 9 (2011): 711–16, https://doi.org/10.3109/09513590.2010.521266.

22. Alina Masters et al., "Melatonin, the Hormone of Darkness: From Sleep Promotion to Ebola Treatment," *Brain Disorders & Therapy* 4, no. 1 (2014): 1000151, https://doi.org/10.4172/2168-975X.1000151.

23. M. Nathaniel Mead, "Benefits of Sunlight: A Bright Spot for Human Health," *Environmental Health Perspectives* 116, no. 4 (2008): A160–67, https://doi.org/10.1289/ehp.116-a160.

24. Dalia M. Kopustinskiene and Jurga Bernatoniene, "Molecular Mechanisms of Melatonin-Mediated Cell Protection and Signaling in Health and Disease," *Pharmaceutics* 13, no. 2 (2021): 129, https://doi.org/10.3390/pharmaceutics13020129.

25. Anne Marie Z. Jukic et al., "Lower 25-Hydroxyvitamin D Is Associated with Long Menstrual Cycles in a Prospective Cohort Study," *Epidemiology* 29, no. 3, (2018): 388–96, https://doi.org/10.1097/EDE.0000000000000804.

26. Ming-Wei Lin and Meng-Hsing Wu, "The Role of Vitamin D in Polycystic Ovary Syndrome," *The Indian Journal of Medical Research* 142, no. 3 (2015): 238–40, https://doi.org/10.4103/0971-5916.166527.

27. June L. Fung et al., "Association of Vitamin D Intake and Serum Levels with Fertility: Results from the Lifestyle and Fertility Study," *Fertility and Sterility* 108, no. 2 (2017): 302–11, https://doi.org/10.1016/j.fertnstert.2017.05.037.

28. Jennifer A. Tamblyn et al., "Vitamin D and Miscarriage: A Systematic Review and Meta-Analysis," *Fertility and Sterility* 118, no. 1 (2022): 111–22, https://doi.org/10.1016/j.fertnstert.2022.04.017.

29. Baker and Driver, "Circadian Rhythms, Sleep, and the Menstrual Cycle."

30. Etymonline, s.v. "Menstruation," by Douglas Harper, accessed December 10, 2023, https://www.etymonline.com/word/menstruation.

31. Lara Schleifenbaum et al., "Women Feel More Attractive before Ovulation: Evidence from a Large-Scale Online Diary Study," *Evolutionary Human Sciences* 3 (2021): e47, https://doi.org/10.1017/ehs.2021.44.

32. Katarzyna Galasinska and Aleksandra Szymkow, "The More Fertile, the More Creative: Changes in Women's Creative Potential across the Ovulatory Cycle," *International Journal of Environmental Research and Public Health* 18, no. 10 (2021): 5390, https://doi.org/10.3390/ijerph18105390.

33. James L. Oschman, Gaétan Chevalier, and Richard Brown, "The Effects of Grounding (Earthing) on Inflammation, the Immune Response, Wound Healing, and Prevention and Treatment of Chronic Inflammatory and Autoimmune Diseases," *Journal of Inflammation Research* 8 (2015): 83–96, https://doi.org/10.2147/JIR.S69656.

34. E. Stobbe et al., "Birdsongs Alleviate Anxiety and Paranoia in Healthy Participants," *Scientific Reports* 12, no. 16414 (2022), https://doi.org/10.1038/s41598-022-20841-0.

35. Myriam Verena Thoma, Ricarda Mewes, and Urs M. Nater, "Preliminary Evidence: The Stress-Reducing Effect of Listening to Water Sounds Depends

on Somatic Complaints: A Randomized Trial," *Medicine* 97, no. 8 (2018): e9851, https://doi.org/10.1097/MD.0000000000009851.

36. Amelia K. Wesselink et al., "Seasonal Patterns in Fecundability in North America and Denmark: A Preconception Cohort Study," *Human Reproduction* 35, no. 3 (March 2020): 565–72, https://doi.org/10.1093/humrep/dez265.

37. Lara S. Franco, Danielle F. Shanahan, and Richard A. Fuller, "A Review of the Benefits of Nature Experiences: More Than Meets the Eye," *International Journal of Environmental Research and Public Health* 14, no. 8 (2017): 864, https://doi.org/10.3390/ijerph14080864.

6. Activating Our Reproductive Qi

1. Susan I. Hopper et al., "Effectiveness of Diaphragmatic Breathing for Reducing Physiological and Psychological Stress in Adults: A Quantitative Systematic Review," *JBI Database of Systematic Reviews and Implementation Reports* 17, no. 9 (2019): 1855–76, https://doi.org/10.11124/JBISRIR-2017-003848.

2. Surabhi Gautam et al., "Yoga—Impact on Mitochondrial Health: Clinical Consequences," *Annals of Neurosciences* 28, no. 3-4 (2021): 114–6, https://doi.org/10.1177/09727531211009431.

3. Geum Joon Cho et al., "Effects of Intensive Training on Menstrual Function and Certain Serum Hormones and Peptides Related to the Female Reproductive System," *Medicine* 96, no. 21, (2017): e6876, https://doi.org/10.1097/MD.0000000000006876.

4. Renae C. Fernandez et al., "Night Shift Among Women: Is It Associated with Difficulty Conceiving a First Birth?," *Frontiers in Public Health* 8 (2020): 595943, https://doi.org/10.3389/fpubh.2020.595943.

5. Helen J. Burgess and Thomas A. Molina, "Home Lighting before Usual Bedtime Impacts Circadian Timing: A Field Study," *Photochemistry and Photobiology* 90, no. 3 (2014): 723–6, https://doi.org/10.1111/php.12241.

6. Heather L. Rusch et al., "The Effect of Mindfulness Meditation on Sleep Quality: A Systematic Review and Meta-Analysis of Randomized Controlled Trials," *Annals of the New York Academy of Sciences* 1445, no. 1 (2019): 5–16, https://doi.org/10.1111/nyas.13996.

7. The Heart–Uterus Connection

1. Sabine Wilms, *Chinese Medicine in Fertility Disorders* (Dannenberg, Germany: Thieme, 2009), 78.

2. Navneet Magon and Sanjay Kalra, "The Orgasmic History of Oxytocin: Love, Lust, and Labor," *Indian Journal of Endocrinology and Metabolism* 15 (2011): S156–61, https://doi.org/10.4103/2230-8210.84851.

3. P. Kumaresan et al., "Human Ovulation and Plasma Oxytocin," *International Journal of Gynaecology and Obstetrics: The Official Organ of the International Federa-*

tion of Gynaecology and Obstetrics 21, no. 5 (1983): 413–18, https://doi.org/10.1016/0020-7292(83)90010-3.

4. V. Rettori et al., "Oxytocin Stimulates the Release of Luteinizing Hormone-Releasing Hormone from Medial Basal Hypothalamic Explants by Releasing Nitric Oxide," *Proceedings of the National Academy of Sciences of the United States of America* 94, no. 6 (1997): 2741–44, https://doi.org/10.1073/pnas.94.6.2741.

5. S. Anjum, A. Anuradha, and A. Krishna, "A Possible Direct Action of Oxytocin on Spermatogenesis and Steroidogenesis in Pre-Pubertal Mouse," *Andrologia* (2018): https://doi.org/10.1111/and.12958.

6. Rollin McCraty and Maria A. Zayas, "Cardiac Coherence, Self-Regulation, Autonomic Stability, and Psychosocial Well-Being," *Frontiers in Psychology* 5 (2014): 1090, https://doi.org/10.3389/fpsyg.2014.01090.

7. Ali M. Alshami, "Pain: Is It All in the Brain or the Heart?," *Current Pain and Headache Reports* 23, no. 12 (2019): 88, https://doi.org/10.1007/s11916-019-0827-4.

8. McCraty and Zayas, "Cardiac Coherence, Self-Regulation, Autonomic Stability, and Psychosocial Well-Being."

9. Chrisanthy Vlachakis et al., "Human Emotions on the Onset of Cardiovascular and Small Vessel Related Diseases," *In Vivo* 32, no. 4 (2018): 859–70, https://doi.org/10.21873/invivo.11320.

10. René Peoc'h, "Psychokinetic Action of Young Chicks on the Path of an Illuminated Source," *Journal of Scientific Exploration* 9, no. 2 (1995): 223–29.

11. Sourya Acharya and Samarth Shukla, "Mirror Neurons: Enigma of the Metaphysical Modular Brain," *Journal of Natural Science, Biology, and Medicine* 3, no. 2 (2012): 118–24, https://doi.org/10.4103/0976-9668.101878.

8. The Magic of Flow

1. Kristin L. Rooney, "The Relationship between Stress and Infertility," *Dialogues in Clinical Neuroscience* 20, no. 1 (2018): 41–47, https://doi.org/10.31887/DCNS.2018.20.1/klrooney.

2. Joe Dispenza, "Demystifying the Formula—Heart Brain Coherence," Unlimited, October 3, 2020, https://drjoedispenza.com/scientific-research/demystifying-the-formula-heart-brain-coherence.

3. Marasha de Jong et al., "Effects of Mindfulness-Based Cognitive Therapy on Body Awareness in Patients with Chronic Pain and Comorbid Depression," *Frontiers in Psychology* 7 (2016): 967, https://doi.org/10.3389/fpsyg.2016.00967.

4. Practice caution if you choose to seek clarity this way, as some sources can be scams and may cause you to doubt your journey, depending on their messages.

5. Lauren Hanna, "#61 What Is Sacred Fertility Yoga? Lauren Hanna Shares Her Inspiring Message on Sacred Conception," interview by Michelle Oravitz, January 7, 2020, in *The Wholesome Fertility Podcast*, podcast, MP3

audio, 52:14, https://www.thewholesomelotusfertility.com/thewholesome
fertilitypodcast/61.

9. The Power of Release

1. Etymonline, s.v. "Emotion," by Douglas Harper, accessed December 10, 2023, https://www.etymonline.com/word/emotion.
2. Leo Newhouse, "Is Crying Good for You?" *Harvard Health Blog*, March 1, 2021, https://www.health.harvard.edu/blog/is-crying-good-for-you-202103 0122020.
3. "A Clean, Well-Lighted Place: How Less Clutter Can Reduce Stress," BeWell, Stanford University, accessed December 11, 2023, https://bewell.stanford.edu/a-clean-well-lighted-place/.

10. Harmonize

1. Reinhold Niebuhr, "The Serenity Prayer."
2. Rachel Towne and Jasenka Grujin, "What Is Kirlian Photography? Aura Photography Revealed," Light Stalking, January 22, 2020, https://www.light stalking.com/what-is-kirlian-photography-the-science-and-the-myth-revealed/; "Kirlian Photography at UCLA," Exact Remedy Academy, March 16, 2015, YouTube video, 3:21, https://youtu.be/mfDHy17QpzY?si=dvpc _JrutP353nOe.
3. Lee Bartel and Abdullah Mosabbir, "Possible Mechanisms for the Effects of Sound Vibration on Human Health," *Healthcare* 9, no. 5 (2021): 597, https://doi.org/10.3390/healthcare9050597.
4. Hyunju Jo et al., "Physiological and Psychological Effects of Forest and Urban Sounds Using High-Resolution Sound Sources," *International Journal of Environmental Research and Public Health*, 16, no. 15 (2019): 2649. https:// doi.org/10.3390/ijerph16152649.

11. Inviting Joy

1. Mimi R. Bhattacharyya et al., "Depressed Mood, Positive Affect, and Heart Rate Variability in Patients with Suspected Coronary Artery Disease," *Psychosomatic Medicine* 70, no. 9 (2008): 1020–7, https://doi.org/10.1097 /PSY.0b013e318189afcc.
2. Sheldon Cohen et al., "Emotional Style and Susceptibility to the Common Cold," *Psychosomatic Medicine* 65, no. 4 (2003): 652–7, https://doi.org /10.1097/01.psy.0000077508.57784.da.
3. JongEun Yim, "Therapeutic Benefits of Laughter in Mental Health: A Theoretical Review," *The Tohoku Journal of Experimental Medicine* 239, no. 3 (2016): 243–9, https://doi.org/10.1620/tjem.239.243.

4. Shevach Friedler et al., "The Effect of Medical Clowning on Pregnancy Rates after In Vitro Fertilization and Embryo Transfer," *Fertility and Sterility* 95, no. 6 (2011), 2127–30, https://doi.org/10.1016/j.fertnstert.2010.12.016.

5. Amie Bouras, "#208 She Was Told She Was Pre-Menopausal before Having Two Babies | Amie Bouras," interview by Michelle Oravitz, November 15, 2022, in *The Wholesome Fertility Podcast*, podcast, MP3 audio, 47:41, https://www.thewholesomelotusfertility.com/thewholesomefertilitypodcast/208.

6. Xianglong Zeng et al., "The Effect of Loving-Kindness Meditation on Positive Emotions: A Meta-Analytic Review," *Frontiers in Psychology* 6 (2015): 1693, https://doi.org/10.3389/fpsyg.2015.01693.

12. We Were Born to Create

1. Deepak Chopra (@DeepakChopra), "The best use of imagination is creativity. The worst use of imagination is anxiety," X (formerly Twitter), September 26, 2012, 9:28 a.m., https://twitter.com/DeepakChopra/status/250980201360678912.

2. George Grouios et al., "The Effect of a Simulated Mental Practice Technique on Free Throw Shooting Accuracy of Highly Skilled Basketball Players," *Journal of Human Movement Studies* 33, no. 3 (1997): 119–38.

3. Gail Matthews, "Goals Research Summary," Dominican University of California, February 2020, https://www.dominican.edu/sites/default/files/2020-02/gailmatthews-harvard-goals-researchsummary.pdf.

13. Surrendering the Blueprint of Our Plan

1. Nancy Weiss, "#152 The Spiritual Side of the Fertility Journey | Nancy Weiss," interview by Michelle Oravitz, October 5, 2021, in *The Wholesome Fertility Podcast*, podcast, MP3 audio, 48:16, https://www.thewholesomelotusfertility.com/thewholesomefertilitypodcast/152.

2. Lisa Miller, "#232 How Life Synchronicities Show Up in the Brain and A Miraculous Fertility Story | Dr. Lisa Miller," interview by Michelle Oravitz, May 2, 2023, in *The Wholesome Fertility Podcast*, podcast, MP3 audio, 44:36, https://www.thewholesomelotusfertility.com/thewholesomefertilitypodcast/232.

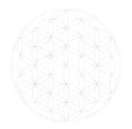

BIBLIOGRAPHY

Acharya, Sourya, and Samarth Shukla. "Mirror Neurons: Enigma of the Metaphysical Modular Brain." *Journal of Natural Science, Biology, and Medicine* 3, no. 2 (2012): 118–24. https://doi.org/10.4103/0976-9668.101878.

Allie. "#119 A Fertility Story of Hope!" Interview by Michelle Oravitz. February 16, 2021, in *The Wholesome Fertility Podcast*. MP3 audio, 40:11. https://www.thewholesomelotusfertility.com/thewholesomefertilitypodcast/119.

Alshami, Ali M. "Pain: Is It All in the Brain or the Heart?" *Current Pain and Headache Reports* 23, no. 12 (2019): 88. https://doi.org/10.1007/s11916-019-0827-4.

Anjum, S., A. Anuradha, and A. Krishna. "A Possible Direct Action of Oxytocin on Spermatogenesis and Steroidogenesis in Pre-Pubertal Mouse." *Andrologia* (2018). https://doi.org/10.1111/and.12958.

Baker, Fiona C., and Helen S. Driver. "Circadian Rhythms, Sleep, and the Menstrual Cycle." *Sleep Medicine* 8, no. 6, (2007): 613–22. https://doi.org/10.1016/j.sleep.2006.09.011.

Bartel, Lee, and Abdullah Mosabbir. "Possible Mechanisms for the Effects of Sound Vibration on Human Health." *Healthcare* 9, no. 5 (2021): 597. https://doi.org/10.3390/healthcare9050597.

Bhasin, Manoj K. "Specific Transcriptome Changes Associated with Blood Pressure Reduction in Hypertensive Patients after Relaxation Response Training." *Journal of Alternative and Complementary Medicine* 24, no. 5 (2018): 486–504. https://doi.org/10.1089/acm.2017.0053.

Bhattacharyya, Mimi R., Daisy L. Whitehead, Roby Rakhit, and Andrew Steptoe. "Depressed Mood, Positive Affect, and Heart Rate Variability in Patients with Suspected Coronary Artery Disease." *Psychosomatic Medicine* 70, no. 9 (2008): 1020–7, https://doi.org/10.1097/PSY.0b013e318189afcc.

Bouras, Amie. "#208 She Was Told She Was Pre-Menopausal before Having Two Babies | Amie Bouras." Interview by Michelle Oravitz, November 15, 2022, in *The Wholesome Fertility Podcast*, MP3 audio, 47:41, https://www.thewholesomelotusfertility.com/thewholesomefertilitypodcast/208.

Burgess, Helen J., and Thomas A. Molina. "Home Lighting before Usual Bedtime Impacts Circadian Timing: A Field Study." *Photochemistry and Photobiology* 90, no. 3 (2014): 723–6. https://doi.org/10.1111/php.12241.

Casper, C., Iryna Sarapuk, and Halyna Pavlyshyn. "Regular and Prolonged Skin-to-Skin Contact Improves Short-Term Outcomes for Very Preterm Infants: A Dose-Dependent Intervention." *Archives de Pédiatrie: Organe Officiel de la Société Française de Pédiatrie* 25, no. 8 (2018): 469–75. https://doi.org/10.1016/j.arcped.2018.09.008.

Chida, Yoichi, and Andrew Steptoe. "The Association of Anger and Hostility with Future Coronary Heart Disease: A Meta-Analytic Review of Prospective Evidence." *Journal of the American College of Cardiology* 53, no. 11 (2009): 936–46. https://doi.org/10.1016/j.jacc.2008.11.044.

Chiu, Sheau-Huey, and Gene Cranston Anderson. "Effect of Early Skin-to-Skin Contact on Mother-Preterm Infant Interaction through 18 Months: Randomized Controlled Trial." *International Journal of Nursing Studies* 46, no. 9 (2009): 1168–80. https://doi.org/10.1016/j.ijnurstu.2009.03.005.

Cho, Geum Joon, Sung Won Han, Jung-Ho Shin, and Tak Kim. "Effects of Intensive Training on Menstrual Function and Certain Serum Hormones and Peptides Related to the Female Reproductive System." *Medicine* 96, no. 21, (2017): e6876. https://doi.org/10.1097/MD.0000000000006876.

Chopra, Deepak (@DeepakChopra). "The best use of imagination is creativity. The worst use of imagination is anxiety." X (formerly Twitter). September 26, 2012. 9:28 a.m. https://twitter.com/DeepakChopra/status/250980201360678912.

"A Clean, Well-Lighted Place: How Less Clutter Can Reduce Stress." BeWell. Stanford University. Accessed December 11, 2023. https://bewell.stanford.edu/a-clean-well-lighted-place/.

Cohen, Sheldon, William Doyle, Ronald B. Turner, Cuneyt M. Alper, and David Skoner. "Emotional Style and Susceptibility to the Common Cold, *Psychosomatic Medicine* 65, no. 4 (2003): 652–7, https://doi.org/10.1097/01.psy.0000077508.57784.da.

Danilenko, Konstantin V., Oksana Y. Sergeeva, and Evgeniy G. Verevkin. "Menstrual Cycles Are Influenced by Sunshine." *Gynecological Endocrinology* 27, no. 9 (2011): 711–16. https://doi.org/10.3109/09513590.2010.521266.

de Jong, Marasha, Sara W. Lazar, Kiran Hug, Wolf E. Mehling, Britta K. Hölzel, Alexander T. Sack, Frenk Peeters, Heidi Ashih, David Mischoulon, and Tim Gard. "Effects of Mindfulness-Based Cognitive Therapy on Body Awareness in Patients with Chronic Pain and Comorbid Depression." *Frontiers in Psychology* 7 (2016): 967. https.//doi.org/10.3389/fpsyg.2016.00967.

Dispenza, Joe. "Demystifying the Formula—Heart Brain Coherence." Unlimited. October 3, 2020. https://drjoedispenza.com/scientific-research/demystify ing-the-formula-heart-brain-coherence.

"Endocrine Disruptors." National Institute of Environmental Health Sciences. Accessed January 3, 2023. https://www.niehs.nih.gov/health/topics/agents/ endocrine.

Fernandez, Renae C., Vivienne M. Moore, Jennifer L. Marino, Melissa J. Whitrow, Michael J. Davies. "Night Shift Among Women: Is It Associated with Difficulty Conceiving a First Birth?" *Frontiers in Public Health* 8 (2020): 595943. https://doi.org/10.3389/fpubh.2020.595943.

Franco, Lara S., Danielle F. Shanahan, and Richard A. Fuller. "A Review of the Benefits of Nature Experiences: More Than Meets the Eye." *International Journal of Environmental Research and Public Health* 14, no. 8 (2017): 864. https://doi.org/10.3390/ijerph14080864.

Friedler, Shevach, Saralee Glasser, Liat Azani, Laurence S. Freedman, Arie Raziel, Dvora Strassburger, Raphael Ron-El, and Liat Lerner-Geva. "The Effect of Medical Clowning on Pregnancy Rates after In Vitro Fertilization and Embryo Transfer." *Fertility and Sterility* 95, no. 6 (2011), 2127–30. https://doi.org/10.1016/j.fertnstert.2010.12.016.

Fung, June L., Terryl J. Hartman, Rosemary L. Schleicher, Marlene B. Goldman. "Association of Vitamin D Intake and Serum Levels with Fertility: Results from the Lifestyle and Fertility Study." *Fertility and Sterility* 108, no. 2 (2017): 302–11. https://doi.org/10.1016/j.fertnstert.2017.05.037.

Galasinska, Katarzyna, and Aleksandra Szymkow. "The More Fertile, the More Creative: Changes in Women's Creative Potential across the Ovulatory Cycle." *International Journal of Environmental Research and Public Health* 18, no. 10 (2021): 5390. https://doi.org/10.3390/ijerph18105390.

Gautam, Surabhi, Rohit Saxena, Tanuj Dada, and Rima Dada. "Yoga—Impact on Mitochondrial Health: Clinical Consequences." *Annals of Neurosciences* 28, no. 3-4 (2021): 114–6. https://doi.org/10.1177/09727531211009431.

Ghazanfarpour, Masumeh, Zahra Atarodi Kashani, Reza Pakzad, Fatemeh Abdi, Fatemeh Alsadat Rahnemaei, Pouran Akhavan Akbari, and Nasibeh Roozbeh. "Effect of Electromagnetic Field on Abortion: A Systematic Review and Meta-Analysis." *Open Medicine* 16, no. 1 (2021): 1628–41. https://doi.org/10.1515/med-2021-0384.

Gooley, Joshua J., Kyle Chamberlain, Kurt A. Smith, Sat Bir S. Khalsa, Shantha M. W. Rajaratnam, Eliza Van Reen, Jamie M. Zeitzer, Charles A. Czeisler, and

Steven W. Lockley. "Exposure to Room Light before Bedtime Suppresses Melatonin Onset and Shortens Melatonin Duration in Humans." *The Journal of Clinical Endocrinology and Metabolism* 96, no. 3 (2011): E463–72. https://doi.org/10.1210/jc.2010-2098.

Grouios, George, Klio Semoglou, Katerina Mousikou, Konstantinos Chatzinikolaou, and Christos Kabitsis. "The Effect of a Simulated Mental Practice Technique on Free Throw Shooting Accuracy of Highly Skilled Basketball Players." *Journal of Human Movement Studies* 33, no. 3 (1997): 119–38.

Gye, Myung Chan, and Chan Jin Park. "Effect of Electromagnetic Field Exposure on the Reproductive System." *Clinical and Experimental Reproductive Medicine* 39, no. 1 (2012), 1–9. https://doi.org/10.5653/cerm.2012.39.1.1.

Hanna, Lauren. "#61 What Is Sacred Fertility Yoga? Lauren Hanna Shares Her Inspiring Message on Sacred Conception." Interview by Michelle Oravitz, January 7, 2020, in *The Wholesome Fertility Podcast*, MP3 audio, 52:14, https://www.thewholesomelotusfertility.com/thewholesomefertilitypodcast/61.

Hanson, Jamie L., Moo K. Chung, Brian B. Avants, Elizabeth A. Shirtcliff, James C. Gee, Richard J. Davidson, and Seth D. Pollak. "Early Stress Is Associated with Alterations in the Orbitofrontal Cortex: A Tensor-Based Morphometry Investigation of Brain Structure and Behavioral Risk." *The Journal of Neuroscience: The Official Journal of the Society for Neuroscience* 30, no. 22 (2010): 7466–72. https://doi.org/10.1523/JNEUROSCI.0859-10.2010.

Hawkins, L. H. Hawkins. "The Influence of Air Ions, Temperature and Humidity on Subjective Wellbeing and Comfort," *Journal of Environmental Psychology* 1, no. 4 (1981): 279–92. https://doi.org/10.1016/S0272-4944(81)80026-6.

Hopper, Susan I., Sherrie L. Murray, Lucille R. Ferrara, and Joanne K. Singleton. "Effectiveness of Diaphragmatic Breathing for Reducing Physiological and Psychological Stress in Adults: A Quantitative Systematic Review." *JBI Database of Systematic Reviews and Implementation Reports* 17, no. 9 (2019): 1855–76. https://doi.org/10.11124/JBISRIR-2017-003848.

Jammoul, Maya, and Nada Lawand. "Melatonin: A Potential Shield against Electromagnetic Waves." *Current Neuropharmacology* 20, no. 3 (2022): 648–60. https://doi.org/10.2174/1570159X19666210609163946.

Jo, Hyunju, Chorong Song, and Yoshifumi Miyazaki. "Physiological Benefits of Viewing Nature: A Systematic Review of Indoor Experiments." *International Journal of Environmental Research and Public Health* 16, no. 23 (2019): 4739. https://doi.org/10.3390/ijerph16234739.

Jo, Hyunju, Chorong Song, Harumi Ikei, Seiya Enomoto, Hiromitsu Kobayashi, and Yoshifumi Miyazaki. "Physiological and Psychological Effects of Forest and Urban Sounds Using High-Resolution Sound Sources." *International Journal of Environmental Research and Public Health*, 16, no. 15 (2019): 2649. https://doi.org/10.3390/ijerph16152649.

Jukic, Anne Marie Z., Allen J. Wilcox, D. Robert McConnaughey, Clarice R.

Weinberg, and Anne Z. Steiner. "Lower 25-Hydroxyvitamin D Is Associated with Long Menstrual Cycles in a Prospective Cohort Study." *Epidemiology* 29, no. 3, (2018): 388–96. https://doi.org/10.1097/EDE.0000000000000804.

Kesari, Kavindra Kumar, Ashok Agarwal, and Ralf Henkel. "Radiations and Male Fertility." *Reproductive Biology and Endocrinology* 16, no. 118 (2018). https://doi.org/10.1186/s12958-018-0431-1.

"Kirlian Photography at UCLA." Exact Remedy Academy. March 16, 2015. YouTube video. 3:21. https://youtu.be/mfDHy17QpzY?si=dvpc_JrutP353 nOe.

Kopustinskiene, Dalia M., and Jurga Bernatoniene. "Molecular Mechanisms of Melatonin-Mediated Cell Protection and Signaling in Health and Disease." *Pharmaceutics* 13, no. 2 (2021): 129. https://doi.org/10.3390/pharmaceutics13020129.

Kumaresan, Perianna, Malathi Kumaresan, Mahmood Hossini, Carolina Arellano, and Alois Vasicka. "Human Ovulation and Plasma Oxytocin." *International Journal of Gynaecology and Obstetrics: The Official Organ of the International Federation of Gynaecology and Obstetrics* 21, no. 5 (1983): 413–18. https://doi.org/10.1016/0020-7292(83)90010-3.

Kurotchenko, S. P., Tatyana I. Subbotina, I. I. Tuktamyshev, I. Sh. Tuktamyshev, A. A. Khadartsev, and A. A. Yashin. "Shielding Effect of Mineral Schungite during Electromagnetic Irradiation of Rats." *Bulletin of Experimental Biology and Medicine* 136, no. 5 (2003): 458–9. https://doi.org/10.1023/b:bebm.0000017092.52535.f8.

Lauretta, Rosa, Andrea Sansone, Massimiliano Sansone, Francesco Romanelli, and Marialuisa Appetecchia. "Endocrine Disrupting Chemicals: Effects on Endocrine Glands." *Frontiers in Endocrinology* 10 (2019). https://doi.org/10.3389/fendo.2019.00178.

Lin, Chunyi. "#71 Qigong Babies? Qigong Master Chunyi Lin Shares His Inspiring Message on the Profound Healing that Arises from Qigong." Interview by Michelle Oravitz. March 17, 2020, in *The Wholesome Fertility Podcast*. MP3 audio, 1:02:19. https://www.thewholesomelotusfertility.com/thewholesomefertilitypodcast/71.

Lin, Ming-Wei, and Meng-Hsing Wu. "The Role of Vitamin D in Polycystic Ovary Syndrome." *The Indian Journal of Medical Research* 142, no. 3 (2015): 238–40. https://doi.org/10.4103/0971-5916.166527.

Magon, Navneet, and Sanjay Kalra. "The Orgasmic History of Oxytocin: Love, Lust, and Labor." *Indian Journal of Endocrinology and Metabolism* 15 (2011): S156–61. https://doi.org/10.4103/2230-8210.84851.

Masters, Alina, Seithikurippu R. Pandi-Perumal, Azizi Seixas, Jean-Louis Girardin, and Samy I. McFarlane. "Melatonin, the Hormone of Darkness: From Sleep Promotion to Ebola Treatment." *Brain Disorders & Therapy* 4, no. 1 (2014): 1000151. https://doi.org/10.4172/2168-975X.1000151.

Matthews, Gail. "Goals Research Summary." Dominican University of California. February 2020. https://www.dominican.edu/sites/default/files/2020-02/gail matthews-harvard-goals-researchsummary.pdf.

McCraty, Rollin, and Maria A. Zayas. "Cardiac Coherence, Self-Regulation, Autonomic Stability, and Psychosocial Well-Being." *Frontiers in Psychology* 5 (2014): 1090. https://doi.org/10.3389/fpsyg.2014.01090.

Mead, M. Nathaniel. "Benefits of Sunlight: A Bright Spot for Human Health." *Environmental Health Perspectives* 116, no. 4 (2008): A160–67. https://doi.org/10.1289/ehp.116-a160.

Miller, Lisa. "#232 How Life Synchronicities Show Up in the Brain and A Miraculous Fertility Story | Dr. Lisa Miller." Interview by Michelle Oravitz, May 2, 2023, in *The Wholesome Fertility Podcast*. MP3 audio, 44:36. https://www.thew holesomelotusfertility.com/thewholesomefertilitypodcast/232.

Niebuhr, Reinhold. "The Serenity Prayer."

Newhouse, Leo. "Is Crying Good for You?" *Harvard Health Blog*. March 1, 2021. https://www.health.harvard.edu/blog/is-crying-good-for-you-2021030122020.

Oschman, James L., Gaétan Chevalier, and Richard Brown. "The Effects of Grounding (Earthing) on Inflammation, the Immune Response, Wound Healing, and Prevention and Treatment of Chronic Inflammatory and Autoimmune Diseases." *Journal of Inflammation Research* 8 (2015): 83–96. https://doi.org/10.2147/JIR.S69656.

Ouyang, Jenny Q., Scott Davies, and Davide Dominoni. "Hormonally Mediated Effects of Artificial Light at Night on Behavior and Fitness: Linking Endocrine Mechanisms with Function." *The Journal of Experimental Biology* 221, no. 6 (2018). https://doi.org/10.1242/jeb.156893.

Patisaul, Heather, ed. "Hormones and Endocrine Disrupting Chemicals: What You Need to Know." Endocrine Society. Accessed December 9, 2023. https://www.endocrine.org/-/media/endocrine/files/patient-engagement/hormones-and-series/hormones_and_edcs_what_you_need_to_know.pdf.

Peoc'h, René. "Psychokinetic Action of Young Chicks on the Path of an Illuminated Source." *Journal of Scientific Exploration* 9, no. 2 (1995): 223–29.

Perez, Vanessa, Dominik D. Alexander, and William H. Bailey. "Air Ions and Mood Outcomes: A Review and Meta-Analysis." *BMC Psychiatry* 13, no. 29 (2013). https://doi.org/10.1186/1471-244X-13-29.

Price, Cynthia J., and Carole Hooven. "Interoceptive Awareness Skills for Emotion Regulation: Theory and Approach of Mindful Awareness in Body-Oriented Therapy (MABT)." *Frontiers in Psychology* 9 (2018): 798. https://doi.org/10.3389/fpsyg.2018.00798.

Reilly, T., and I. C. Stevenson. "An Investigation of the Effects of Negative Air Ions on Responses to Submaximal Exercise at Different Times of Day." *Journal of Human Ergology* 22, no. 1 (1993): 1–9.

"Research on Endocrine Disruptors." United States Environmental Protection Agency. Last modified July 11, 2023. https://www.epa.gov/chemical-research/research-endocrine-disruptors.

Rettori, V., Griselda Canteros, Roger Reinoso, M. Gimeno, and S. M. McCann. "Oxytocin Stimulates the Release of Luteinizing Hormone-Releasing Hormone from Medial Basal Hypothalamic Explants by Releasing Nitric Oxide." *Proceedings of the National Academy of Sciences of the United States of America* 94, no. 6 (1997): 2741–44. https://doi.org/10.1073/pnas.94.6.2741.

Rooney, Kristin L. "The Relationship between Stress and Infertility." *Dialogues in Clinical Neuroscience* 20, no. 1 (2018): 41–47. https://doi.org/10.31887/DCNS .2018.20.1/klrooney.

Rusch, Heather L., Michael Rosario, Lisa M. Levison, Anlys Olivera, Whitney S. Livingston, Tianxia Wu, and Jessica M. Gill. "The Effect of Mindfulness Meditation on Sleep Quality: A Systematic Review and Meta-Analysis of Randomized Controlled Trials." *Annals of the New York Academy of Sciences* 1445, no. 1 (2019): 5–16. https://doi.org/10.1111/nyas.13996.

Schleifenbaum, Lara, Julie C. Driebe, Tanja M. Gerlach, Lars Penke, and Ruben C. Arslan. "Women Feel More Attractive before Ovulation: Evidence from a Large-Scale Online Diary Study." *Evolutionary Human Sciences* 3 (2021): e47. https://doi.org/10.1017/ehs.2021.44.

Stobbe, Emil, Josefine Sundermann, Leonie Ascone, and Simone Kühn. "Birdsongs Alleviate Anxiety and Paranoia in Healthy Participants." *Scientific Reports* 12, no. 16414 (2022). https://doi.org/10.1038/s41598-022-20841-0.

Sun, Ying, Peijun Ju, Ting Xue, Usman Ali, Donghong Cui, and Jinghong Chen. "Alteration of Faecal Microbiota Balance Related to Long-Term Deep Meditation." *General Psychiatry* 36, no. 1 (2023): e100893. https://doi.org/10.11 36/gpsych-2022-100893.

Suzuki, Satoko, Shinya Yanagita, Seiichiro Amemiya, Yumi Kato, Natsuko Kubota, Tomoo Ryushi, and Ichiro Kita. "Effects of Negative Air Ions on Activity of Neural Substrates Involved in Autonomic Regulation in Rats." *International Journal of Biometeorology* 52, no. 6 (2008): 481–9. https://doi.org/ 10.1007/s00484-007-0143-2.

Tamblyn, Jennifer A., Nicole S.P. Pilarski, Alexandra D. Markland, Ella J. Marson, Adam Devall, Martin Hewison, Rachel K. Morris, Arri Coomarasamy. "Vitamin D and Miscarriage: A Systematic Review and Meta-Analysis." *Fertility and Sterility* 118, no. 1 (2022): 111–22. https://doi.org/10.1016/j.fertnstert .2022.04.017.

Tan, Dun-Xian, Lucien C. Manchester, Lilan Qin, and Russel J. Reiter. "Melatonin: A Mitochondrial Targeting Molecule Involving Mitochondrial Protection and Dynamics." *International Journal of Molecular Sciences* 17, no. 12 (2016): 2124. https://doi.org/10.3390/ijms17122124.

Thoma, Myriam Verena, Ricarda Mewes, and Urs M. Nater. "Preliminary

Evidence: The Stress-Reducing Effect of Listening to Water Sounds Depends on Somatic Complaints: A Randomized Trial." *Medicine* 97, no. 8 (2018): e9851. https://doi.org/10.1097/MD.0000000000009851.

Towne, Rachel, and Jasenka Grujin. "What Is Kirlian Photography? Aura Photography Revealed." Light Stalking. January 22, 2020. https://www.lightstalking.com/what-is-kirlian-photography-the-science-and-the-myth-revealed/.

Vlachakis, Chrisanthy, Konstantina Dragoumani, Sofia Raftopoulou, Meropi Mantaiou, Louis Papageorgiou, Spyridon Champeris Tsaniras, Vasileios Megalooikonomou, and Dimitrios Vlachakis. "Human Emotions on the Onset of Cardiovascular and Small Vessel Related Diseases." *In Vivo* 32, no. 4 (2018): 859–70. https://doi.org/10.21873/invivo.11320.

Webster, Noah J., Kristine J. Ajrouch, and Toni C. Antonucci. "Towards Positive Aging: Links between Forgiveness and Health." *OBM Geriatrics* 4, no. 2 (2021). https://doi.org/10.21926/obm.geriatr.2002118.

Weiss, Nancy. "#152 The Spiritual Side of the Fertility Journey | Nancy Weiss." Interview by Michelle Oravitz, October 5, 2021, in *The Wholesome Fertility Podcast*. MP3 audio, 48:16. https://www.thewholesomelotusfertility.com/thewholesomefertilitypodcast/152.

Wesselink, Amelia K., Lauren A. Wise, Elizabeth E. Hatch, Ellen M. Mikkelsen, Henrik T. Sørensen, Anders H. Riis, Craig J. McKinnon, and Kenneth J. Rothman. "Seasonal Patterns in Fecundability in North America and Denmark: A Preconception Cohort Study." *Human Reproduction* 35, no. 3 (March 2020): 565–72. https://doi.org/10.1093/humrep/dez265.

Wilms, Sabine. *Chinese Medicine in Fertility Disorders*. Dannenberg, Germany: Thieme, 2009.

Xu, You-Qiong, Bao-Hua Li, and Huai-Min Cheng. "High-Frequency Electromagnetic Field Exposure on Reproductive and Endocrine Functions of Female Workers." *Chinese Journal of Industrial Hygiene and Occupational Diseases* 26, no. 6 (2008): 332–5. https://pubmed.ncbi.nlm.nih.gov/18771615/.

Yim, JongEun. "Therapeutic Benefits of Laughter in Mental Health: A Theoretical Review." *The Tohoku Journal of Experimental Medicine* 239, no. 3 (2016): 243–9. https://doi.org/10.1620/tjem.239.243.

Zeng, Xianglong, Cleo P. K. Chiu, Rong Wang, Tian P. S. Oei, and Freedom Y. K. Leung. "The Effect of Loving-Kindness Meditation on Positive Emotions: A Meta-Analytic Review." *Frontiers in Psychology* 6 (2015): 1693. https://doi.org/10.3389/fpsyg.2015.01693.

Zimmerman, Scott, and Russel J. Reiter. "Melatonin and the Optics of the Human Body." *Melatonin Research* 2, no. 1 (Feb. 2019): 138–60. https://doi.org/https://doi.org/10.32794/mr11250016.

ABOUT THE AUTHOR

Michelle Oravitz is an acupuncturist specializing in fertility health whose own life was transformed by acupuncture. While she began her career as an architect of buildings, Michelle's healing journey through natural medicine revealed her divine purpose: becoming an architect of human health and happiness.

Michelle's experience helping couples conceive taught her that conception is not only a physical event but also simultaneously exists in other dimensions of being. She believes that this same life-giving energy, with love at its core, is what draws us to fulfill our dharma, or highest purpose. Michelle believes that aligning with the highest self and living in accordance with the laws of nature are what bring about optimal life force vitality. She teaches her patients that reproductive health reflects this vitality and naturally improves as a result of coming into harmony with nature's laws.

Michelle is the host of *The Wholesome Fertility Podcast,* a top-rated podcast she started in 2018. On *The Wholesome Fertility Podcast,* she interviews leading experts and best-selling authors such as Dr. Christiane Northrup, Dr. Bruce Lipton, and Dr. Alice Domar and provides her own fertility wellness tips to her listeners. She has also been endorsed by best-selling authors such as Dr. Christiane Northrup and Jessica Ortner and has been featured on other top-rated fertility podcasts and in numerous publications.

During her free time, Michelle enjoys spending time with her family as well as reading, doing yoga, meditating, and painting.

Facebook: https://www.facebook.com/thewholesomelotus

X (Twitter): https://twitter.com/Wholesomelotus

Instagram: https://www.instagram.com/thewholesomelo tusfertility

YouTube: https://www.youtube.com/c/TheWholesomeFer tilityChannel

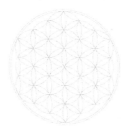

THANK YOU FOR READING!

Thank you for taking this journey with me. My hope is that the information and exercises I shared not only get you closer to your baby, but also inspire you to live your best life.

If you'd like to implement a deeper level of practice through hypnosis and meditations, I'd like to gift you a free 7-day trial to my Fertility Hypnosis & Mindset Library, which can be found here:

https://www.michelleoravitz.com/Fertilitymindsetmembership

Made in United States
North Haven, CT
24 October 2024

59366201R00136